# The NHS
## 2009/10

Peter Davies

The eleventh edition of The NHS handbook.

First, second, third, fourth, fifth, sixth, seventh, eighth, ninth (then called The Pocket Guide) and tenth editions published by:

The NHS Confederation
29 Bressenden Place
London SW1E 5DD
Tel: 020 7074 3200
Fax: 0870 487 1555

To order further copies of this handbook or other Confederation publications, contact our publications sales team on 0870 444 5841 or visit www.nhsconfed.org/publications

978-1-85947-164-7

Printed in the UK in April 2009. The information included correct at time of print.

Design by Grade Design Consultants, London
www.gradedesign.com

POC00501

This publication has been manufactured using paper produced under the FSC Chain of Custody. It is printed using vegetable-based inks and low VOC processes by a printer employing the ISO14001 environmental accreditation.

FSC
Mixed Sources
Product group from well-managed forests and other controlled sources
Cert no. SA-COC-001904
www.fsc.org
© 1996 Forest Stewardship Council

# Contents

Please contact us on 0870 444 5841 for more information about the versions of the *NHS handbook 2009/10* suitable for those with a visual impairment.

# Sponsor's foreword

The Appointments Commission is delighted to be working in partnership with the NHS Confederation and to be sponsoring the *NHS handbook 2009/10*.

These are challenging times for the health service as we seek to place quality at the heart of everything we do while recognising that now, more than ever before, the effective use of public resources is essential.

Excellent leadership will be needed at all levels in the health service to meet these challenges and to ensure that the services we commission and provide reach the high standards our communities have every right to expect.

At the Appointments Commission we understand the complexity of the NHS and recognise that it requires the best possible people to lead its boards. Recent events have demonstrated the necessity of good governance in complex organisations and the importance of the strategic drive, scrutiny and constructive challenge that strong, independent chairs and non-executive directors can bring. Our understanding ensures that we are uniquely positioned to attract, appoint and help you retain world-class chairs and non-executive directors to work alongside executive colleagues and deliver excellent healthcare.

We work with the full range of NHS stakeholders, including strategic health authorities, primary care trusts, foundation trusts, acute, mental health and ambulance trusts to guide them through the public appointments process. With a wealth of experience and knowledge, our teams provide tailored recruitment and selection services to ensure that the requirements of these important roles are fully understood and the best possible people appointed.

This *NHS handbook* is a valuable guide in understanding the health service; as we all strive towards meeting the challenges of quality and leadership, the more we understand about our NHS the more we are able to improve it.

**Andrea Sutcliffe**
Chief Executive, Appointments Commission
www.appointments.org.uk

# Foreword

Welcome to the 2009/10 edition of *The NHS handbook*, your guide to today's NHS. Whether you have a wealth of NHS experience or are new to health, this essential guide will steer you around the complexities of the health service and give you all the information you need in one handy reference source.

Among what's new for this year is information about the NHS Constitution, CQC and registration, and preparing for a flu pandemic.

The NHS recently celebrated its 60th anniversary and looks forward to the NHS of the future following publication of health minister Lord Darzi's NHS Next Stage Review. The review report set out a new foundation for a health service that empowers staff and gives patients choice.

The NHS Confederation continues to shape and influence all the essential components of a flourishing health service – everything from commissioning and providing services, financing and staffing the NHS, to the NHS across the UK and Europe. Strong leadership in all areas of the NHS is more important than ever and we continue to look at how it can be strengthened.

Once again, the handbook is supported by advertising from selected organisations already working alongside the NHS Confederation. In particular I am very grateful to the Appointments Commission, who have kindly agreed to support this year's edition.

We are always pleased to receive comments on the handbook and hear any suggestions for future editions. Please contact our publications team on 020 7074 3200 or email publications@nhsconfed.org with any such feedback.

**Steve Barnett**
Chief Executive, NHS Confederation

THE **NHS** CONFEDERATION

The NHS Confederation is the only independent membership body for the full range of organisations that make up today's NHS. We represent over 95 per cent of NHS organisations as well as a growing number of independent healthcare providers.

Our ambition is a health system that delivers first-class services and improved health for all. We work with our members to ensure that we are an independent driving force for positive change by:
• influencing policy, implementation and the public debate
• supporting leaders through networking, sharing information and learning
• promoting excellence in employment.

### How do we work?
• We offer a range of services to meet the shared needs of our members and provide a collective voice for the whole of the NHS. NHS Employers is part of the NHS Confederation and represents our members on workforce issues.
• We have a family of networks that focus on meeting the specific needs of our members and provide a distinct voice for NHS trusts, foundation trusts, PCTs, ambulance trusts, mental health trusts and independent sector providers.

We also run the NHS European Office to inform NHS organisations of key EU developments and to promote the interests of the NHS in Europe. The Welsh NHS Confederation and the Northern Ireland Confederation support members in their countries and we provide a subscription service for NHS organisations in Scotland.

### How to join
Our membership fees are based on your organisation's annual turnover. Membership fees for independent sector providers are based on the organisation's income from delivering services directly to patients on behalf of the NHS. For an additional fee, NHS Confederation members can join the network most appropriate to their sector.

### Further information
www.nhsconfed.org
membership@nhsconfed.org

# Introduction
## One system – four structures

The National Health Service is based on common principles throughout the four constituent parts of the United Kingdom, although its structure in each is quite distinctive – and increasingly so. Ever since the NHS's foundation more than 60 years ago, it has adapted its shape to the particular administrative and geographical conditions of England, Scotland, Wales and Northern Ireland. But since devolution in 1999, and the transfer of responsibility for healthcare in Scotland, Wales and Northern Ireland to the Scottish Parliament, Welsh Assembly and the Northern Ireland Assembly, the divergence in structure has become more marked. The NHS has also pursued different priorities in each of the four countries.

UK population (2007)

|  | (million) | % of total |
| --- | --- | --- |
| England | 51.09 | 83.8 |
| Scotland | 5.14 | 8.4 |
| Wales | 2.98 | 4.9 |
| Northern Ireland | 1.76 | 2.9 |
| **Total** | **60.97** | **100** |

Source: Office for National Statistics

Vital statistics: NHS spending per head in the UK 2007/08 (£)

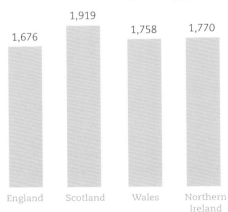

1,676 England
1,919 Scotland
1,758 Wales
1,770 Northern Ireland

Sources: UK health departments

However, the service's underlying values remain the same. These originate from the 1944 white paper, *A national health service*, which stated that:

> The government ... want to ensure that in future every man, woman and child can rely on getting all the advice and treatment and care they may need in matters of personal health; that what they shall get shall be the best medical and other facilities available; that their getting these shall not depend on whether they can pay for them or any other factor irrelevant to the real need.

Both society and the health service have altered almost beyond recognition since then, but the NHS still strives to provide a broadly comprehensive service, mostly free to all at the point of need.

Of course, it has had to move with the times to take advantage of scientific and technological advances, as well as political, social and economic change. Major reform programmes have been under way in all four parts of the UK for most of the past decade, although certain principles remain common to all four systems. On the NHS's 60th anniversary in July 2008, the four UK health ministers declared that 'the NHS belongs to all the people of England, Scotland, Wales and Northern Ireland', and affirmed their commitment to a statement of common principles:

- the NHS provides a comprehensive service, available to all
- access to its services is based on clinical need, not an individual's ability to pay
- the NHS aspires to high standards of excellence and professionalism
- NHS services must reflect the needs and preferences of patients, their families and their carers
- the NHS works across organisational boundaries with other organisations in the interests of patients, communities and the wider population
- the NHS is committed to providing the best value for taxpayers' money, making the most effective and fair use of finite resources
- the NHS is accountable to the public, communities and patients that it serves.

Earlier in 2008, health ministers from Scotland, Wales and Northern Ireland had agreed a 'joint statement on NHS values' that stressed the service was 'based on strong partnerships between the Government, the public, patients, staff and their trade unions'. In England, the NHS Constitution (page 115) formally sets out the service's overarching principles as well as specifying rights and pledges to patients and the public.

## What the NHS does

In a typical year, people in England visit GP practices 300 million times, make 19 million visits to accident and emergency departments and over 5 million calls to NHS Direct. There are more than 4 million ordinary and day case admissions to hospital, and more than 45 million outpatient appointments. People also attend 1.2 million appointments with independent inpatient, day case and surgical outpatient services, and make over 3 million visits to independent outpatient services.

### What the NHS does: contacts per day (thousands)

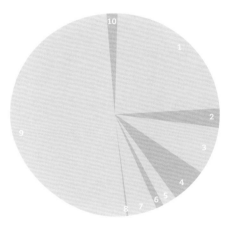

1 Total community contacts 389 (24%)
2 A&E attendances 49 (3%)
3 Outpatient attendances 124 (7%)
4 In bed as emergency admission to hospital 94 (6%)
5 In bed as elective admission to hospital 36 (2%)
6 NHS Direct calls 18 (1%)
7 Courses of NHS dental treatments for adults 73 (4%)
8 Walk-in centres 6
9 GP or practice nurse consultations 836 (51%)
10 NHS sight tests 28 (2%)

Figures are for England only.
Source: Department of Health

# 01 The structure of the NHS in England

Ultimate responsibility for the NHS lies with Parliament. At a strategic level, the Department of Health is one of the largest central government departments; it is assisted nationally by a range of 'arm's-length bodies' and regionally by the strategic health authorities. At an operational level, primary care trusts occupy a pivotal position as local commissioning organisations, while NHS trusts, foundation trusts and – increasingly – independent healthcare organisations provide the services. A chain of accountability therefore runs from local bodies up through the regions to Government and Parliament.

## Parliament

As the NHS is financed mainly through taxation it relies on Parliament for its funds, and has to account to Parliament for their use through the Secretary of State for Health, the cabinet member responsible for the service. Parliament scrutinises the service through debates, MPs' questions to ministers and select committees. These procedures mean that the Government has to publicly explain and defend its policies for the NHS. The Scottish Parliament (page 228), the Welsh Assembly (page 250) and the Northern Ireland Assembly (page 266) are responsible for oversight of the NHS in their parts of the UK. Health services in the Isle of Man and the Channel Islands are not part of the NHS.

### Select committees

Three select committees, each comprising backbench MPs representing the major parties, are particularly relevant to the NHS. They are all able to summon ministers, civil servants and NHS employees to give oral or written evidence to their inquiries, usually in public. Their reports are published throughout the parliamentary session.

### Health committee

The health committee's role is 'to examine the expenditure, administration and policy of the Department of Health and its associated bodies'. It has a maximum of 11 members. Recent inquiries have covered patient safety, health inequalities and foundation trusts.
www.parliament.uk

### Public accounts committee

The public accounts committee scrutinises all public spending and is concerned with ensuring the NHS is operating with economy, efficiency and effectiveness. Its inquiries are based on reports about the service's 'value for money', produced by the Comptroller and Auditor General,

who heads the National Audit Office. It aims to draw lessons from past successes and failures that can be applied to future activity. The committee has 16 members, and is traditionally chaired by an Opposition MP. Recent inquiries examined the GP contract and neonatal services.
www.parliament.uk
www.nao.gov.uk

### Public administration committee
The public administration committee examines reports from the Health Service Commissioner (better known as the Ombudsman, see page 159). Its remit now includes responsibility for scrutinising third sector policy (see page 34). It has 11 members.
www.parliament.uk
www.ombudsman.org.uk

### Health ministers
Six ministers, all appointed by the Prime Minister to the Department of Health, are responsible in Parliament for health and social care. They provide the DH with political leadership and are responsible for making the main executive decisions on:
- strategy
- overall policy framework
- framework of laws
- performance objectives for the DH and for the public services for which they are responsible
- agreeing overall resource levels with the Chancellor and the Prime Minister
- priorities for distributing resources, based on the strategy and policy framework.

Ministers do not generally become involved in local decisions or individual cases (although exceptions do occur), and should not be involved in DH-related decisions about their own constituencies.

The DH's ministers comprise the Secretary of State, three ministers of state – responsible for health services, public health and care services respectively – and two parliamentary under-secretaries of state, one of whom sits in the House of Lords. The Secretary of State is a member of the cabinet and has overall responsibility for NHS and social care delivery, system reforms, finance, resources and strategic communications. The other ministers each have specific areas of NHS activity assigned to them. The Department for Children, Schools and Families has the lead for children's issues, and the Department for Work and Pensions has the lead for issues affecting older people. Both work closely with the Department of Health.

## The Department of Health

The Department of Health provides strategic leadership to the NHS and social care organisations in England, setting their overall direction while deciding and monitoring standards. It does not directly provide health or social care services itself, but is responsible for the stewardship of £90 billion of public money.

The DH's three strategic objectives are:
• better health and well-being: helping people stay healthy, empowering them to live independently and tackling health inequalities
• better care: ensuring the best possible, safe and effective health and social care, provided when and where people need it
• better value: delivering affordable, efficient and sustainable services, contributing to the wider economy and the nation.

In effect the DH is the national headquarters of the NHS, negotiating funding with the Treasury and allocating resources to the health service at large. The DH's running costs in 2008/09 were estimated at £219m. Its 2,245 core staff are based mainly in London and Leeds but also in the nine Government Offices for the Regions. The DH receives on average more parliamentary questions than any other Whitehall department, as well as 8 per cent of all Freedom of Information requests and nearly 100,000 letters and e-mails a year.

The Scottish Government Health Directorates (page 230), the Welsh Department for Health and Social Services (page 252) and Northern Ireland's Department of Health, Social Services and Public Safety (page 267) provide strategic leadership for the NHS in their parts of the UK. However, the DH has UK-wide responsibility for international and European Union business and for:
• co-ordinating plans to cope with a flu pandemic
• licensing and safety of medicines and medical devices
• ethical issues such as abortion and embryology.

## Further information

*The DH guide: a guide to what we do and how we do it*, DH, December 2007.
*Department of Health Business Plan 2008–09*, DH, April 2008.
*Departmental report: the health and personal social services programmes*, DH, May 2008.
www.dh.gov.uk

## Managing the DH

The DH's ability to meet the challenges it faces was assessed – along with all other government departments – by the Cabinet Office in 2007 in an exercise that will be repeated in 2009. In response the DH produced a development plan and reorganised its internal management.

## Three senior leaders

Its three most senior staff, all of equal rank, are the permanent secretary, NHS chief executive and chief medical officer. These posts are not political appointments and do not change with a change of government. (The permanent secretary and NHS chief executive roles were combined in 2000 but then separated again in 2006.) The permanent secretary is responsible for running the department day-to-day. The NHS chief executive is responsible for the service's management and performance. Both are responsible to the Secretary of State. The DH's chief medical officer is the UK Government's principal medical adviser and the professional head of all medical staff in England (there are also CMOs for Scotland, Wales and Northern Ireland).

The chief executive's report on the NHS is published each year and outlines the service's progress towards meeting key objectives. The CMO publishes an annual independent report to Parliament on the state of the nation's health.

## Further information

*Capability review of the Department of Health*, Cabinet Office, June 2007.
*Department of Health development plan*, DH, September 2007.
*The year 2007/08: NHS chief executive's annual report*, DH, May 2008.
*On the state of public health: annual report of the chief medical officer 2008*, DH, March 2009.

## Department of Health organisation chart

Departmental board members

Source: Department of Health

## Departmental board

The departmental board meets about six times a year and focuses on major strategic cross-cutting issues facing the DH. It is supported by other boards and committees (see page 19) with defined responsibilities for areas of the DH's business. It is responsible for:

- advising ministers on strategy and objectives for the health and social care system
- setting DH standards
- establishing the framework of governance, assurance and risk management
- the departmental business plan
- the resource account for each financial year
- the departmental report
- major expenditure commitments.

Its members are:

- permanent secretary, who chairs the board
- NHS chief executive
- chief medical officer
- director general of social care, local government and care partnerships
- director general of DH finance and operations
- three non-executive directors.

## Corporate management board

The CMB provides corporate leadership. Its six or seven meetings each year are scheduled around the annual business planning and quarterly performance management cycle. Members are:

- permanent secretary, who chairs the board
- NHS chief executive, who has a standing invitation
- chief medical officer, who has a standing invitation
- chief nursing officer
- NHS medical director
- associate NHS medical director, Office of the Chief Medical Officer
- director general, health improvement and protection
- director general, health inequalities
- director general, research and development
- director general, communications
- director general, DH finance and operations
- director general, social care, local government and care partnerships
- director general, policy and strategy
- director general, NHS finance, performance and operations
- director general, commissioning and system management
- director general, workforce.

The CMB's policy committee meets every six weeks and is responsible for advice on priorities, resources and the overall policy programme. Its corporate management and improvement committee focuses on capability, planning, performance and risk management, corporate policy-making, internal communication, environmental, reputation and social issues.

## NHS management board and executive groups

This board brings together monthly all strategic health authority chief executives and the NHS chief executive's leadership team of DH directors-general. It provides leadership for the NHS and is responsible for ensuring the service's performance and financial delivery are on track. Members are:

- NHS chief executive, who chairs the board
- permanent secretary
- chief medical officer
- chief nursing officer
- director general, social care, local government and care partnerships
- director general, commissioning and system management
- director general, workforce
- director general, DH finance and operations
- director general, NHS finance, performance and operations

- director general, communications
- NHS medical director
- director general, policy and strategy
- director of NHS communications
- director, Office of the SHAs
- chief of staff
- chief adviser to the NHS chief executive
- NHS chief information officer
- chief executives of the ten SHAs.

Five executive groups meet regularly to bring together DH and NHS staff with expertise and experience to make decisions and drive change, led by the relevant DH director general. These groups cover:
- commissioning and system management
- finance, performance and operations
- people matters
- clinical matters
- informatics.

### NHS Leadership Council

The Next Stage Review (see page 113) recommended setting up an NHS Leadership Council to help nurture the next generation of NHS leaders and build a strong culture of leadership across the service. Key work will include:
- gathering intelligence and evidence
- setting standards
- taking a strategic role in commissioning leadership development programmes
- ensuring leadership capacity is improved across the NHS.

The council will be a sub-committee of the NHS management board with up to 18 members, including five part-time leads for the priority areas of clinical leadership, top leaders, board development, emerging leaders and inclusion.

### Audit committee

The audit committee advises senior departmental leaders on risk management, corporate governance and assurance arrangements in the DH and its subsidiary bodies. Members include DH senior managers and non-executive members drawn from NHS, social care, Department of Children, Families and Schools, and independent bodies. The committee meets quarterly and is chaired by a non-executive member.

## Committee of the regions

This committee oversees delivery of the DH's public service agreements (see page 117) through local government and its contribution to the performance framework for local authorities. It also agrees health and social care priorities with the regional directors of public health. It meets quarterly.

## Performance committee

The performance committee meets four or five times a year and monitors performance against departmental strategic objectives, public service agreements, value for money, critical programmes and projects and financial targets on the department board's behalf.

## Chief professional officers

The DH's chief professional officers provide expert knowledge in specialist health and social care disciplines to ministers, other government departments and the Prime Minister. They comprise:
• chief medical officer
• chief nursing officer
• chief dental officer
• chief health professions officer
• chief pharmaceutical officer
• chief scientific officer.

## Department of Health board structure

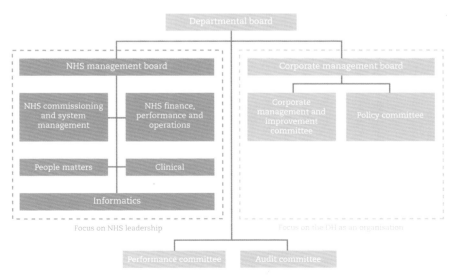

Source: Department of Health

## National clinical directors

National clinical directors are clinical specialists and figureheads for specific national service frameworks (see page 128), representing the interests of the NHS and social care within the DH. Focused on delivering care rather than DH policy, their most important role is spearheading change by engaging with professionals and providing leadership.

The clinical directors are led by the NHS medical director, a post created in 2007. They meet monthly and also:
- visit health and social care practitioners
- chair taskforces with health and social care professionals and health service managers
- work with the Royal Colleges to ensure that changes in health and social care are reflected in training and education
- chair taskforces to develop national service frameworks that bring together health professionals, service users and carers, health service managers, partner agencies, and other advocates.

They are:
- national clinical director for emergency access
- national clinical director for trauma care
- national director for mental health
- national director for health and work
- national director for heart disease and stroke
- national clinical director for primary care
- national director of pandemic influenza preparedness
- national director for widening participation in learning
- national clinical director for diabetes
- national clinical director for kidney services
- national clinical director for cancer
- national clinical director for transplant
- national director for equality and human rights
- national clinical director for children, young people and maternity services
- national clinical director for hospital pharmacy
- national clinical director for community pharmacy
- co-national director for learning disabilities.

# Arm's-length bodies

Arm's-length bodies (ALBs) are stand-alone national organisations with executive functions, sponsored by the Department of Health. They vary in size but tend to have boards, employ staff and publish accounts. They include special health authorities (see below) and also:

- two executive agencies, the Medicines and Healthcare Products Regulatory Agency and NHS Purchasing and Supply Agency; these are part of the DH and accountable to it
- non-departmental public bodies, which are set up when ministers want independent advice without direct influence from Whitehall departments.

ALBs are accountable to the DH and sometimes directly to Parliament. They have existed since the NHS was set up in 1948. ALBs have been cut in number from 38 to 20 in the last five years. Their roles are:

- regulating the health and social care system and workforce
- establishing national standards and protecting patients and public
- providing central services to the NHS.

The National Audit Office has confirmed that the DH is on track to meet the key targets in its review of ALBs, with a 27 per cent reduction in posts and £250 million annual savings.

**Further information**

*Releasing resources to the frontline: the Department of Health's review of its arm's length bodies*, National Audit Office, January 2008.

*Department of Health's public bodies 2008*, DH, December 2008.

# Special health authorities

Special health authorities provide a service to the whole of England rather than to a local community. They are independent, but can be subject to ministerial direction like other NHS bodies. They currently comprise:

- National Institute for Health and Clinical Excellence
- National Patient Safety Agency
- National Treatment Agency for Substance Misuse
- NHS Blood and Transplant
- NHS Business Services Authority
- NHS Litigation Authority
- NHS Professionals
- Information Centre for Health and Social Care
- NHS Institute for Innovation and Improvement.

## Department of Health and its partners

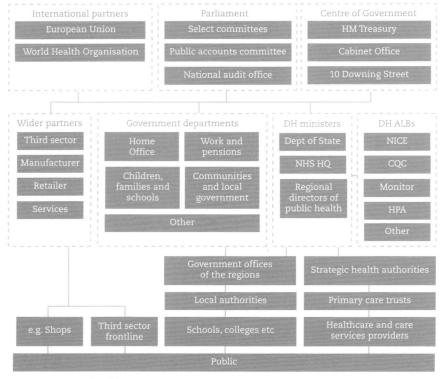

Source: Department of Health

## Strategic health authorities

In England, strategic health authorities (SHAs) have acted as the local headquarters of the NHS since their creation in 2002. Originally 28 in number, they were reduced to ten in 2006. They do not deliver services, but provide leadership, co-ordination and support across a defined geographical area, managing the performance of PCTs and NHS trusts. (For management arrangements in Scotland, see page 232; Wales, page 254; and Northern Ireland, page 268.) SHAs are almost coterminous with the Government Offices for the English Regions (see page 64). SHAs draw up plans to recruit, retain and develop NHS staff, and they devise financial solutions for service needs. They also work with partner organisations in local government, education and the charitable and voluntary sector.

## Strategic health authorities

North
East

Yorkshire and
the Humber

North
West

East
Midlands

West
Midlands

East of
England

South
Central  London

South East
Coast

South West

Source: Department of Health

Their three main tasks are:
- developing strategy to clarify short, medium and long-term priorities
- managing and improving performance, establishing performance
  agreements with all local NHS organisations and redesigning care
  processes to focus on patient pathways
- building capacity and capability in terms of people, facilities and
  buildings within and across organisations.

Following the Next Stage Review (see page 113), SHAs will also have a
legal duty to promote innovation, holding regional innovation funds for
that purpose.

The Office of the Strategic Health Authorities (OSHA) was set up in 2003 to help SHAs work collectively. Its core functions are:
• providing SHAs with a joint executive
• providing a focal point for their relationships with the DH and other national bodies
• helping them share learning and experience.

The SHAs fund OSHA jointly, and the ten SHA chief executives meet monthly to manage their business through the office.
www.osha.nhs.uk

## Primary care trusts

In England, primary care trusts (PCTs) are the cornerstone of the NHS locally. Their equivalents in Scotland, community health partnerships, manage primary and community health services. Wales's seven new local health boards are responsible for managing primary and secondary services. Since April 2009 Northern Ireland has had five local commissioning groups driven by GPs.

The 152 PCTs (reconfigured in 2006 from 303) oversee England's 29,000 GPs and 18,000 dentists. They have an average population of 330,000 and are responsible for over 80 per cent of the NHS budget; ten have budgets of over £1 billion each. About 70 per cent of them are coterminous with the 150 social care departments.

PCTs' main functions are:
• improving the health of their population – reducing health inequalities in partnership with the local authority; protecting health; emergency planning
• commissioning services, including hospital care, mental health, GP practices, screening programmes, patient transport, NHS dentists, pharmacies and opticians – assessing need, reviewing provision and deciding priorities; designing services; shaping supply through placing contracts; managing demand and performance-managing providers
• developing staff skills, investing capital in buildings, equipment and IT.

PCTs have provided a wide range of out-of-hospital services directly but are being required to separate commissioning and provider functions by 2010. As a result of the Next Stage Review, staff will have a 'right to request' to set up social enterprises (see page 35) to provide services. PCT boards will be obliged to consider such requests and – if the PCT board approves the business case – support the social enterprise by awarding it an initial three-year contract to provide services.

**Further information**
*Primary care trusts: serving communities*, NHS Confederation, 2006.
*Leading edge 21: What sort of organisation for PCT provider functions?*,
NHS Confederation, October 2007.
*Transforming community services: enabling new patterns of provision*, DH, January 2009.

**Spotlight on policy: NHS Local**

PCTs are now able to change their names by adopting the NHS prefix
before their place name: for example, Blackpool PCT is now known as
NHS Blackpool. PCTs and others had questioned whether the PCT name
adequately reflected their role. PCTs felt that as they are responsible for
the vast majority of NHS expenditure in their areas, their title should
convey that they are a major NHS presence in a locality.

Renaming PCTs in this way enables them to position themselves as
frontline commissioners of patient care and be identifiable to their local
populations as such – an integral objective of 'world-class commissioning'
(see page 42). The PCT title was not thought to be well understood, and
the new style will potentially improve their recognition. Care trusts are
unaffected by the change.

**Further information**
*NHS Brand Guidelines* **www.nhsidentity.nhs.uk**

**Teaching PCTs**

Teaching PCTs (tPCTs), set up mainly in areas of deprivation or where
it has been difficult to recruit, are able to offer GPs and other health
professionals clinical posts that involve teaching, research or
development. They are not confined to traditional teaching activities such
as postgraduate clinical training, continuing professional development
and lifelong learning, but aim to provide activities that encompass the
ethos of learning, development, research, dissemination and good practice.
By offering this type of career development, tPCTs hope to attract
additional high-quality staff, particularly to deprived areas.

After the 2006 reconfiguration, tPCTs did not automatically keep their
teaching status but had to seek approval from their SHA. There are
currently 29 tPCTs out of the total of 152 PCTs.

## NHS trusts

NHS trusts in England numbered about 130 in 2008, of which the largest
category – about 90 – is acute trusts, followed by mental health trusts,
which number about 25. There are also 11 ambulance trusts. These
numbers are approximate as the total of NHS trusts is shrinking as
more are granted foundation trust status.

NHS trusts were abolished in Scotland in 2004. Wales will abolish trusts in
2009, except for its ambulance service and another trust providing specialist
services, while Northern Ireland has now reduced its 18 trusts to five.

NHS trusts earn their income through providing healthcare commissioned
by PCTs and practice-based commissioners, which is paid for on a
'payment by results' basis (see page 175). They have a legal duty to break
even financially, earn a 6 per cent return on their capital and achieve
minimum quality standards. They must work in partnership with other
NHS organisations, local authorities, independent providers and the
voluntary sector. Trusts are also obliged to deliver national priorities.

Although strategic health authorities manage their performance, trusts
are largely self-governing organisations. Their boards comprise a chair, five
non-executive directors and five executives – including the chief executive
and usually the medical, nursing and finance directors.

## Foundation trusts

Foundation trusts are designed to give greater freedoms to NHS organisations,
as part of the wider programme of moving from a service controlled
nationally to one where standards and inspection are national but delivery
and accountability are local. They are unique to the NHS in England.

They are independent public benefit organisations, modelled on co-operatives and mutual societies, but remain part of the NHS – subject to its standards, performance ratings and inspection systems. Foundation trusts are still accountable to Parliament, but local people have a say in running them by becoming members or governors (see page 147).

Monitor, the independent regulator of foundation trusts (see page 158), authorises NHS trusts applying for foundation status and ensures they comply with the terms of their authorisation. Monitor is accountable to Parliament but independent of the Health Secretary, and has powers to intervene in the running of a foundation trust if it fails to meet standards or breaches the terms of its authorisation. The Care Quality Commission (see page 158) is responsible for inspecting the performance of foundation trusts, as it is for all other NHS organisations.

Foundation trusts' main advantages include:
- increased freedom to retain any operating surpluses – for example, from land sales – and access to capital from both the public and private sectors; the amount a foundation trust can borrow is determined by a formula based on its ability to repay the loan, and governed by the prudential borrowing code set by Monitor
- an obligation to achieve national targets and standards like the rest of the NHS, but freedom to decide how they do this
- not being subject to directions from the Secretary of State
- powers to establish private companies
- the ability to vary staff pay from nationally agreed terms and conditions, although Agenda for Change (see page 197) does apply to foundation trusts
- not being subject to performance management by strategic health authorities and the DH.

By April 2009 there were 117 foundation trusts, representing half of all acute and mental health trusts. Foundation trusts employ more than 375,000 staff. Some have revenues as high as £600 million and in size and complexity are equivalent to FTSE 250 private sector companies. As part of the FT/FTSE link project launched in 2006, 14 foundation trusts now have partnerships with such companies.

The Next Stage Review called for the rate at which NHS trusts achieve foundation status to be accelerated, and the Government expects all to achieve it by December 2010. In early 2009 SHAs anticipated about 20 trusts would not be ready by the deadline, with six ready only on the deadline. Where Monitor finds that an NHS trust may never be financially viable as a foundation trust, the trust may face closure or merger instead. Six PCTs are exploring the possibility of becoming 'community foundation trusts', which could provide some of the community services currently run by PCTs.

### Further information
*Marketing matters: successes, challenges and lessons from NHS foundation trusts,* Foundation Trust Network/NHS Confederation, April 2008.
*Towards autonomy: lessons from aspirant community foundation trusts,* Primary Care Trust Network/NHS Confederation, April 2008.
*A powerful partnership,* Foundation Trust Network/FTSE link project, July 2008.
*NHS foundation trusts: review and consolidated accounts 2007–08,* Monitor, October 2008.
*Foundation trusts and Monitor: sixth report of session 2007–08,* House of Commons health committee, October 2008.
*Applying for NHS foundation trust status: guide for applicants,* Monitor/DH, December 2008.
Monitor **www.regulator-nhsft.gov.uk**

**Key organisation: Foundation Trust Network**
The Foundation Trust Network (FTN) was established as part of the NHS Confederation to provide a distinct and independent voice for NHS foundation trusts in England. Set up in 2004, membership includes nearly all authorised foundation trusts and over 90 aspirant foundation trusts. The network aims to raise the profile of the issues facing existing and aspirant foundation trusts and to improve the influence of FTN members. Its work programme is steered by an independent board of non-executive directors elected by its members, and an executive director appointed by the board.
**www.nhsconfed.org/Networks/Foundationtrust**

## Care trusts
Care trusts are designed to allow close integration of health and social care (a measure unnecessary in Northern Ireland where the two services are fully integrated). They commission and provide both within a single NHS organisation.

The NHS and local authority may establish a care trust together where both agree it offers the best way to improve health and social care. NHS and local authority health-related functions are delegated to the trust, not transferred, and the arrangement is voluntary – partners can withdraw. Local authority councillors are members of the care trust's board. Care trusts may be based on either a primary care trust or an NHS trust.

The concept is intended to be flexible enough to allow for a range of models and service configurations, but care trusts are likely to focus on specialist mental health and older people's services. Among the total of 152 PCTs, ten are care trusts, two of which have foundation status. However, there are increasing examples of PCT and adult social care coming together in shared management arrangements, although not generally using the care trust organisational mode.

## Children's trusts

The Government's long-term aim, as stated in the 2004 green paper, *Every child matters*, is to integrate key children's services within a single organisational focus, the preferred model for which is children's trusts. Children's trusts are not legal entities but partnerships between organisations that provide, commission or are involved in services for children and young people. They are normally led by local authorities. A children's trust has the following core features:
• clear short- and long-term objectives
• a children's services director in overall charge of delivering these objectives
• a single planning and commissioning function, supported by pooled budgets.

The trust should involve children and families in putting together a picture of their needs and in designing the services to meet those needs through public, private, voluntary and community providers.

The Government announced in the Children's Plan that it intended to strengthen children's trusts, extending the number of their partners and making their boards statutory bodies.

**Further information**
*The children's plan: building brighter futures*, DCSF, December 2007.
*Are we there yet? Improving governance and resource management in children's trusts*, Audit Commission, October 2008.
*What is a children's trust?* DCSF, November 2008.

## Independent providers

By using independent providers – private sector companies, voluntary organisations and social enterprises – to offer care to NHS patients, the health service can expand capacity and improve choice. The Government also believes that competition from a plurality of providers acts as an incentive to the NHS to improve its response to patients' needs.

Since April 2008, health service patients have had free choice of any hospital or treatment centre in England that meets NHS standards and costs, including those in the independent sector. This innovation was the culmination of several years of policy-making. In 2002 the Government declared: 'The NHS cannot remain a monolithic, centrally run monopoly provider', and predicted that 'Working with providers from the independent sector and from overseas is not a temporary measure. They will become a permanent feature of the new NHS landscape and will provide NHS services. Different healthcare providers will work to a common ethos, common standards and a common system of inspection.'

From 2006, any patient needing secondary care was entitled to choose from at least four hospitals. This was then broadened so that patients could choose from an 'extended choice network' that comprised any foundation trust or nationally approved independent sector provider; the network numbered 147 by the end of 2008. As patient choice was widened further, independent sector providers meeting eligibility criteria for taking NHS patients formed a 'free choice network'. For routine elective care, 'any willing provider' may now offer to supply services.

Now that the Government has established the principle of independent sector provision in the NHS, it expects to play less of a lead role in encouraging its take-up, passing the initiative to local commissioners. In 2007 the DH stated: 'For acute elective provision, the extent of independent sector provision will be patient-led. For other services, it will be commissioner-led. We expect commissioners to recognise and make appropriate use of independent sector providers to optimise patient care across all sectors.'

The Government's emphasis on common values was reiterated in the Next Stage Review: 'Patients expect that wherever they receive their NHS-funded treatment, the same values and principles should apply. All organisations are part of an integrated system for the benefit of patients'.

By mid-2007, 300 NHS patients a month chose to be treated in private hospitals, costing £620,000 a month; a year later this had risen to 3,634 – about 1 per cent of elective cases – at a cost of £7.6 million.

**Further information**
*Growing capacity: a new role for external healthcare providers in England*, DH, June 2002.
*Creating a patient-led NHS – delivering the NHS Improvement Plan*, DH, March 2005.
*Creating a level playing field: a fair environment for patient care*, NHS Confederation, 2006.
*Independent providers ... making a difference in the NHS*, NHS Confederation, 2006.
*New providers: new solutions – the independent sector partnering with the NHS*,
NHS Confederation, February 2009.

## The private sector
Traditionally, private healthcare providers in the UK tended to concentrate on secondary care, but with Government encouragement they and new entrants to the market are now looking for opportunities in primary care too. They have also become major suppliers of diagnostic services to the NHS.

The Government initially encouraged private sector companies to set up treatment centres (see page 91) to carry out elective surgery and diagnostic tests for NHS patients under five-year contracts. This has paved the way for them gradually to play a bigger role, and volumes of services they provide to the NHS are now rising rapidly.

**Further information**
*ISTCs and the NHS: sticking plaster or real reform?* CBI, February 2008.

**Key organisation: NHS Partners Network**
The NHS Partners Network (NHSPN) was established in 2005 and incorporated into the NHS Confederation in June 2007. The network is an alliance of independent (commercial and not-for-profit) healthcare providers involved in all aspects of NHS care at primary, secondary or acute level, including diagnostic and specialist treatment centres. It aims to help independent sector providers become a fully accepted part of a mixed economy NHS that seeks to offer greater patient choice and value for money for patients, taxpayers and shareholders. Its work programme is steered by an independent board elected by its members.
www.nhsconfed.org/Networks/NHSPartners

## The third sector

'Third sector' describes the range of institutions that fall between the public and private sectors. These include small local community and voluntary groups, large and small registered charities, foundations, trusts, co-operatives and social enterprises. They often provide inpatient and outpatient mental health services, sexual health services, drug rehabilitation and palliative care. Many smaller voluntary organisations play a crucial part in community services, particularly for vulnerable and excluded groups, and are often able to bridge divides between statutory services. PCTs are being encouraged to ensure third sector organisations are included in the planning process. The aim is that third sector organisations can become 'equal players' in providing services.

DH research into the third sector's potential contribution in 2007 found 35,000 third sector organisations provided health or social care, and another 1,600 planned to do so. Total funding for these services amounted to £12 billion a year, with just over half from the public sector – 36 per cent of which was for healthcare and 62 per cent for social care.

The DH has set up a third sector investment programme, which has two funding schemes for 2009/10:
- the strategic partner programme will recruit up to ten third sector organisations to act as strategic partners and advocates for their sector
- the innovation, excellence and service development fund will finance projects with potential for national impact.

### Further information

*No excuses. Embrace partnership now. Step towards change! Report of the third sector commissioning task force*, DH, July 2006.
*Third sector mapping report*, DH, February 2007.
*Eleventh report of session 2007–08: public services and the third sector: rhetoric and reality*, House of Commons public administration committee, July 2008.
*Partnership in public services: the public services action plan one year on*, Cabinet Office, August 2008.
*NHS Next Stage Review: what it means for the third sector*, DH, December 2008.
Office of the Third Sector **www.cabinetoffice.gov.uk/thirdsector**
Third sector investment programme **www.dh.gov.uk/thirdsectorinvestment**

## Vital statistics: NHS spending on non-NHS healthcare (£m)

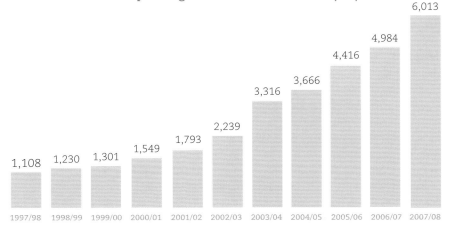

| 1997/98 | 1998/99 | 1999/00 | 2000/01 | 2001/02 | 2002/03 | 2003/04 | 2004/05 | 2005/06 | 2006/07 | 2007/08 |
|---------|---------|---------|---------|---------|---------|---------|---------|---------|---------|---------|
| 1,108 | 1,230 | 1,301 | 1,549 | 1,793 | 2,239 | 3,316 | 3,666 | 4,416 | 4,984 | 6,013 |

Source: Department of Health

### Social enterprises

Social enterprises are organisations run on business lines, but which reinvest profits in the community or in service developments.

The Government sees encouragement for social enterprise in health and social care as key to reforms. Social enterprises take different forms, and may include co-operatives, trusts or community interest companies. They are estimated to number at least 55,000, have a combined turnover of £27 billion a year and account for 1 per cent of GDP. Social enterprises involve patients and staff in designing and delivering services, improving quality and tailoring services to meet patients' needs. Many feature partnerships with third sector organisations (see page 34).

Under the 'right to request' commitment in the Next Stage Review, PCT boards are obliged to consider requests from staff to set up a social enterprise and, if approved, support its development.

The DH's £100 million social enterprise investment fund helps social enterprises develop initiatives such as women's refuges, migraine clinics and exercise programmes for elderly people. The DH's Innovation for Life Challenge Fund, developed with the Social Enterprise Coalition, invites health and social care commissioners to propose innovative ways of using social enterprises. Strategic health authorities can bid for up to £100,000 revenue funding to help commission cross-sector social enterprise solutions.

**Further information**

*Social enterprise – making a difference: a guide to the right to request*, DH, November 2008.
Social Enterprise Coalition **www.socialenterprise.org.uk**

# Working in partnership

The concept of partnership has become a cornerstone of policy for modernising institutions across the whole field of civil and public life. It is one of the NHS's 'common principles' (see page 10), and partnership arrangements – with local government, the voluntary and private sectors and indeed with patients and the public – are a central feature of health and social care policy.

At national level, the DH, NHS organisations – represented by NHS Employers – and trade unions work together under a 'partnership agreement' and meet in the Social Partnership Forum (see page 192) to discuss workforce issues. This underpins the National Stakeholder Forum, a high-level strategic group covering broad policy development and implementation. At a more local level, strategic health authorities are responsible for ensuring social partnerships are developed.

## Local strategic partnerships (LSPs)

LSPs are intended to:
- bring together the different parts of the public sector and the private, business, community and voluntary sectors
- enable strategic decisions to be taken while still being close enough to neighbourhoods to allow decisions to be made at community level
- create strengthened, empowered, healthier and safer communities.

The NHS has a key role to play in LSPs and neighbourhood renewal by improving health and reducing health inequalities.

The core tasks of LSPs are to:
- develop and deliver a local neighbourhood renewal strategy to secure more jobs, better education, improved health, reduced crime and better housing, narrowing the gap between deprived neighbourhoods and the rest and contributing to the national targets to tackle deprivation
- prepare and implement a community strategy for the area, identify and deliver the most important things that need to be done, keep track of progress and keep it up to date

- bring together local plans, partnerships and initiatives to provide a forum through which mainstream service providers (local authorities, police, health services, central government agencies and bodies outside the public sector) work effectively together to meet local needs and priorities
- work with local authorities that are developing a local area agreement (see page 54) to help devise and meet suitable targets.

## Government departments

A range of government departments – apart from the DH – has responsibilities that impinge on health, and work in partnership with the NHS. They include:

- **Communities and Local Government**: responsible for housing, regional and local government.
www.communities.gov.uk
- **Home Office**: lead responsibility for progress on the drug strategy; the Home Secretary chairs the cross-government cabinet ministerial sub-committee on drugs policy; local crime and disorder reduction partnerships.
www.homeoffice.gov.uk/drugs
www.drugs.gov.uk
- **Department for Children, Schools and Families**: responsible for children's social care policy, the Change for Children programme, Every Child Matters strategy and Sure Start, which aims to improve health, education and emotional development for young children in disadvantaged areas. The Healthy Schools programme is run jointly with the DH.
www.dcsf.gov.uk
www.surestart.gov.uk
- **Department for Environment, Food and Rural Affairs**: responsibilities include water, farming, fisheries, horticulture and some aspects of rural health and well-being. Protection from the effects of pollution or toxic chemicals are particular concerns.
www.defra.gov.uk

# Put these dates in your diary...

## NHS Confederation annual conference and exhibition

10 – 12 June 2009, Liverpool
23 – 25 June 2010, Liverpool

**www.nhsconfed.org**

## NHS Employers annual conference and exhibition

3 – 5 November 2009, Birmingham

**www.nhsemployers.org**

# 02 Commissioning

Commissioning is the process by which the NHS decides what services are needed, acquires them and then ensures they are being provided appropriately. It involves assessing the population's needs and deciding which are priorities, procuring the services to meet them and managing the providers. If done effectively, it ultimately ensures people live healthier and longer lives.

The origins of commissioning can be traced to the advent of the internal market in 1991 and the division of the NHS into purchasers and providers. Then it was referred to as 'purchasing'. The past decade's reforms have altered the nature of commissioning. Today the new GP contract, payment by results, the tariff and patient choice have all contributed to its evolution – and mean it must continue to develop and adapt. 'World-class commissioning' represents the latest generation – an attempt to create a new form of commissioning and lead the way internationally.

Responsibility for commissioning rests mainly with primary care trusts in partnership with general practice (see practice-based commissioning, page 50) and local government. Joint commissioning with local government brings together PCTs and social care services for strategic planning and development.

## The basics

### Essential elements
The essential elements of sound commissioning are:
- assessing needs – based on rigorous analysis
- reviewing service provision – identifying gaps and potential for improving existing services
- deciding priorities – the PCT should produce a strategic plan for the health community
- designing services – practices work individually or in groups to develop strategies and models to improve services
- strategic plans – signalling the strategic direction for local services and highlighting commissioning priorities over the next five years
- shaping the structure of supply – PCTs must be clear about the services and specifications needed, and agree contracts with local providers within the new national contracting framework
- managing demand and ensuring appropriate access to care – practices and PCTs should establish strategies for the use of care and resources

- clinical decision-making – individual practices and clinicians undertake individual needs assessments, make referrals and advise patients on choices and treatments
- managing performance – practices must manage their indicative budget to maximise the benefits from available resources
- patient and public feedback – PCTs are responsible for measuring and reporting on patients' experience.

In particular, the Government wants to see commissioning:
- shift towards services that are personal, sensitive to individual need and that maintain independence and dignity
- re-orient towards promoting health and well-being, investing to reduce the future costs of ill health
- focus more on services and interventions that will achieve better health, across health services and local government, promote inclusion and tackle health inequalities.

**Further information**
*Health reform in England: update and commissioning framework*, DH, July 2006.
*Commissioning framework for health and wellbeing*, DH, March 2007.

## Setting priorities

The ability to identify priorities is a key skill for commissioners. Many NHS resources still reflect historic patterns of provision or the particular approach of local providers, or even of individual clinicians. To break free of this requires systematic, evidence-based decisions about what treatments and services to commission. The number of high-cost treatments and increasingly vocal interest groups make allocating resources a politically sensitive and complex issue. Need and demand for healthcare always have and always will exceed the NHS's available funds – which means that PCTs must prioritise needs into those that will be met and those that will not.

PCTs stand a better chance of arriving at fair decisions that properly balance competing needs if their priority setting shows:
- a sound grasp of the concept – to reduce uncertainty and risk
- organisational cohesion – so that everyone in the PCT understands how priorities are set and therefore makes consistent decisions
- consistency – especially in relation to individual funding requests
- protocol-driven decision-making – which is consistent, efficient and timely, as PCTs repeatedly face the same scenarios.

**Further information**

*Priority setting: an overview*, Primary Care Trust Network/NHS Confederation, October 2007.
*Priority setting: managing new treatments*, PCTN/NHS Confederation, February 2008.
*Priority setting: managing individual funding requests*, PCTN/NHS Confederation, March 2008.
*Priority setting: legal considerations*, PCTN/NHS Confederation, March 2008.
*Priority setting: strategic planning*, PCTN/NHS Confederation, April 2008.

## World-class commissioning

Although the NHS introduced commissioning in 1991, it is generally recognised that it has never had a chance to mature as a discipline, unlike hospital management. As a result, and despite pockets of excellence, there is an imbalance in the influence that providers and commissioners exert over the system. 'World-class commissioning' is a response to that: it seeks to transform how the NHS goes about commissioning, redressing the balance. It represents the most serious attempt to reposition commissioning as central to the way the NHS operates. In particular it aims to make full use of the advantages that the NHS – as a publicly funded system free to all – offers commissioners: it can provide rich clinical data that, if used to its potential, could have a direct impact on individuals and the population as a whole, reducing inequalities in health. As the Next Stage Review expressed it: 'The world-class commissioning programme is designed to raise ambitions for a new form of commissioning that delivers better health and well-being for the population, improving health outcomes and reducing health inequalities – adding life to years and years to life.'

World-class commissioning focuses on assessing and prioritising population needs, strategic outcomes, procuring services and managing providers to deliver the required outcomes. It requires a longer-term, and more strategic approach than hitherto. PCTs need to:
• lead the NHS locally
• work with community partners
• engage with public and patients
• collaborate with clinicians
• manage knowledge and assess needs
• prioritise investment
• stimulate the market
• promote innovation and improvement
• secure procurement skills

- manage the local health system
- make sound financial investments.

An assurance system, managed by SHAs, recognises and rewards performance and ensures milestones are reached while allowing PCTs to set local priorities. It specifies a level all PCTs have to reach in the short term and one they will need to achieve over time. PCTs published the first results of the assurance process in February 2009.

**Further information**
*World class commissioning: vision*, DH, December 2007.
*World class commissioning: competencies*, DH, December 2007.
*World class commissioning assurance handbook*, DH, June 2008.
*Briefing 164: World-class commissioning assurance*, NHS Confederation, June 2008.
*Achieving the competencies: practical tips for NHS commissioners*, DH, September 2008.
*The role of the PCT board in world class commissioning*, DH, November 2008.
www.dh.gov.uk/worldclasscommissioning

**Support for commissioning: FESC**
The Framework for procuring External Support for Commissioners (FESC) comprises 14 private sector companies that PCTs can call on for support with their world-class commissioning endeavours. They offer specialist expertise in services such as data analysis and contract management, which is not always widely available in PCTs. The Healthcare Commission found in 2006 that 'many PCTs do not fully understand the health needs of their local people, making it difficult for them to buy targeted services'.

Each company has been appointed to FESC by the DH on the basis of its technical and commercial ability. PCTs remain responsible for managing the services provided. A FESC-appointed commissioning supplier cannot be a provider of clinical services in the same PCT area. Several FESC schemes are being piloted across the country to demonstrate various ways in which the framework might be used. The Next Stage Review's interim report (see page 113) commented that 'given the variation in NHS commissioning skills currently on offer', there should be 'extensive use within every SHA' of FESC.

# Commissioning and competition

There is no general requirement for NHS services to be subject to formal procurement: provision of healthcare in the UK has usually not involved contracts enforceable in the courts but 'NHS contracts' agreed between organisations belonging to the health service. But as the use of independent and third sector providers for NHS-funded services has become more common, and foundation trusts have become established – with which contracts are legally binding – a formal procurement process must now be followed in some circumstances.

In addition, the 2006 commissioning framework required commissioners to review services systematically, focusing initially on any where quality caused concern; this could lead to a decision to tender a service that failed to meet standards or failed to improve. Since then, the introduction of free choice of provider for patients and the opportunity for any willing provider to supply services has further increased competition to supply services.

With this growing diversity of providers, the DH has formulated principles and rules to ensure competition is fair and transparent, and safeguard the NHS's reputation. It has also set up a panel to enforce the rules and a website for commissioners and providers to publicise opportunities to tender for services.

## Principles and rules of competition

The ten core principles underlying the rules comprise transparency, objectivity, proportionality, non-discrimination, subsidiarity, consistency, and no double jeopardy. The rules are:

- Services should be commissioned from providers best placed to meet patients' needs.
- Providers and commissioners must co-operate to ensure patients experience a seamless service regardless of organisational boundaries, and to ensure continuity and sustainability.
- Commissioning and procurement should be transparent and non-discriminatory.
- Commissioners and providers should foster patient choice and ensure patients have accurate and reliable information to exercise it.
- Promotional activity is encouraged if it is consistent with patients' best interests and the NHS's reputation.
- Providers must not discriminate against patients and must promote equality.
- Payment regimes must be transparent and fair.

- Financial intervention in the system must be transparent and fair.
- Mergers, acquisitions, de-mergers and joint ventures are acceptable when in patients' and taxpayers' best interests and when there remain sufficient choice and competition to ensure high standards of care and value for money.
- Vertical integration is permissible when in patients' and taxpayers' best interests, as long as it protects the primacy of the GP gatekeeper function and there remain sufficient choice and competition to ensure high standards and value for money.

**Further information**
*Principles and rules for co-operation and competition*, DH, December 2007.
*Framework for managing choice, co-operation and competition*, DH, May 2008.
*PCT procurement guide for health services*, DH, May 2008.

## Code of practice for promoting services
The code sets out rules for promotional material issued by providers of NHS services, whether they are from within the NHS, third sector or private sector. Its 46 clauses aim to ensure that information patients receive is not misleading, inaccurate, unfair or offensive. It is also designed to protect the NHS brand and reputation, and ensure spending on promotion is not excessive. PCTs are responsible for enforcing the code through their contracts, overseen by SHAs. Where they cannot resolve a dispute, the matter can be referred to the NHS Co-operation and Competition Panel or, if appropriate, to the Advertising Standards Authority.

**Further information**
*Code of practice for the promotion of NHS-funded services*, DH, March 2008.

## NHS Co-operation and Competition Panel
The panel, set up in 2009, is designed to ensure competition between the NHS and independent sector for NHS-funded services is fair and transparent. It advises SHAs, the DH and Monitor on resolving disputes, and is responsible for considering complaints about procurement of clinical services, advertising and promotion, and the merger or acquisition of healthcare providers where an NHS body is involved. It only considers disputes not resolved locally.
www.ccpanel.org.uk

## NHS Supply2Health

This website helps PCTs advertise health and social care services they wish to commission and enables suppliers to identify business opportunities in the NHS. All NHS commissioners must post information about tendering opportunities and contract awards here, making it easier for suppliers to locate single opportunities and understand what PCTs want. Supply2Health helps commissioners meet their European Union and other legal requirements to advertise, and potentially increases responses to adverts by reaching a wider audience. It also offers e-mail alerts when new opportunities are posted. Supply2Health covers both health and social care, which may be commissioned jointly with the local authority. www.supply2health.nhs.uk

# PCTs and commissioning

The Next Stage Review called for all PCTs to commission comprehensive well-being and prevention services in partnership with local authorities, personalised to meet the local population's needs.

## Commissioning primary care

The current primary medical care contracting arrangements were introduced in 2004 to enable the NHS to provide a wider range of services closer to where patients live and improve the quality of care. PCTs have four options for commissioning primary care services.

• They can use the nationally agreed general medical services (GMS) contract (see page 198) to determine the services a GP practice will provide. Revised in 2003, the GMS contract has since evolved in partnership between NHS Employers and the British Medical Association's GP Committee. It allows GPs flexibility over the services they offer. It has enabled some to reduce their workload – important in helping the NHS recruit and retain GPs – while others have taken on new services; remuneration is adjusted accordingly. Practices have to provide essential services – which means treating sick and terminally ill patients – but can opt out of providing 'additional' services such as child immunisation, maternity and contraceptive services and cervical tests. Most have maintained or expanded the range of services they provide.

- PCTs can use a locally agreed arrangement with practices, the personal medical services (PMS) contract. This enables them to offer salaried appointments to GPs, particularly useful where it has been difficult to recruit and retain them using the GMS contract. PMS contract terms are decided between the PCT and GP to tailor services to local needs. Almost half of GPs now work to PMS contracts.

- Under the alternative provider medical services (APMS) arrangements, PCTs can contract with non-NHS bodies such as voluntary or commercial sector providers to supply primary medical services. They may also contract with NHS secondary care organisations – foundation trusts, NHS trusts – or other PCTs for them to provide primary care services. The Government sees APMS as offering substantial opportunities for restructuring services for greater patient choice, improved access and greater responsiveness to specific community needs. It believes APMS can be a valuable tool in areas that have always been underprovided with primary care, where practices have opted out of providing some services or in areas finding it difficult to recruit GPs.

- Finally, PCTs can provide services themselves (PCTMS), employing GPs and their practice staff and taking on practice lists and services.

PCTs also hold dental and pharmacy contracts in order to ensure provision of these services locally.

Where PCTs encounter problems securing adequate GP services, the DH insists they 'actively commission additional practices' from diverse suppliers, including the independent sector. 'Change will be driven locally, with local authority input, and co-ordinated nationally in a series of procurement waves', it said in the white paper, *Our health, our care, our say*. It promised to ensure that 'the principles of contestability and value for money are realised under a fair, transparent and consistent process'.

**Further information**
NHS Primary Care Contracting (employers' web area): **www.pcc.nhs.uk**

**Spotlight on policy: Improving access to GP services**

In 2006/07 the largest ever patient survey on access to GP services found significant variations across the country and pockets of dissatisfaction. Although 84 per cent were happy with their GP practice's opening hours, half who were not wanted their practice to open on a Saturday and a quarter wanted it to open on a weekday evening. Some deprived areas had too few doctors: one had 43 serving 100,000 people, while the England average is 61 and one area had as many as 88. People from black and minority ethnic groups expressed particular problems with access to GPs.

As a result, the Government announced:
- an improvement team to help practices and PCTs that need support to strengthen their GP services
- PCTs would produce local action plans to improve access to GP services where problems exist
- better information for patients about practices, including opening hours and details of patients' experiences to be included on the NHS Choices website (see page 222).

In addition, the Government made available £250 million to provide 112 new practices in the quarter of PCTs with the worst provision, as well as one new GP-led health centre in each PCT. The first of these health centres – run by a social enterprise – opened at the end of 2008 in Bradford, and sees patients from 8am to 8pm, seven days a week. Patients may use the centre and stay registered with their own GP.

By January 2009, 71 per cent of the 8,258 GP practices in England were offering extended opening hours following changes to the GP contract to encourage them to do so.

**Further information**
*Access all areas: improving GP and primary care access*, NHS Confederation, April 2008.
*No patient left behind: how can we ensure world class primary care for black and minority ethnic people?*, DH, May 2008.
*Report of the National Improvement Team for Primary Care Access and Responsiveness*, DH, May 2008.
*The GP patient survey 2007/08*, NHS Information Centre, July 2008.

## Commissioning acute, mental health and community services

Since 2008/09 PCTs have had to use the standard NHS contract for acute hospital services in their agreements with providers for acute hospital-based care. This covers NHS trusts, new foundation trusts, existing foundation trusts whose contracts have expired and new agreements with independent sector providers.

The aim is to ensure fairness and avoid a confusing mixture of contract types. The contract is based on the ten principles for co-operation and competition (see page 44). It contains several sanctions:
- financial adjustments for breaches of the 18-week waiting-time target
- non-payment for inappropriate excess activity
- withholding payment for failure to supply required information
- financial adjustments for breaches of the target to reduce the healthcare-associated infection C. *difficile*.

From April 2009, PCTs will also use new standard contracts to commission community, mental health and ambulance services, based on many of the same principles as the acute services contract.

### Further information
*The standard NHS contracts for acute hospital, mental health, community and ambulance services and supporting guidance*, DH, December 2008.

## Commissioning specialised services

Specialised services are those with low patient numbers but which need a critical mass of patients to make treatment centres cost-effective. They are provided in relatively few specialist centres to catchment populations of more than 1 million people, and are subject to different commissioning arrangements from other NHS services. As they are high-cost, low-volume treatments, the risk to an individual PCT of having to fund expensive, unpredictable activity is reduced by PCTs grouping together to commission such services collectively and sharing financial risk.

Commissioning arrangements for specialised services were strengthened following an independent review led by Sir David Carter during 2006/07. Specialised services are either commissioned regionally, by ten specialised commissioning groups (SCGs), or nationally by the National Commissioning Group (NCG), depending on the rarity of the condition or treatment.

Each SCG is aligned with a strategic health authority and acts on behalf of a population of about 5 million people. They commission – for example – haemophilia services and blood and marrow transplantation.

The NCG advises ministers on which NHS services are best commissioned nationally rather than locally. Most services it commissions relate to conditions suffered by fewer than 400 people nationally. Examples include heart and lung transplantation and secure forensic mental health services for adolescents. The NCG's annual budget is about £350 million.

In addition, the National Specialised Commissioning Group (NSCG) oversees national commissioning and encourages SCGs to collaborate. SCG chairs – usually PCT chief executives – form NSCG's core membership.

**Further information**
www.specialisedcommissioning.nhs.uk
National Commissioning Group **www.ncg.nhs.uk**
National Specialised Commissioning Group **www.nscg.nhs.uk**

## Practice-based commissioning

Practice-based commissioning is a reform designed to give GPs and practice nurses more say in how the NHS provides services for patients. The Government regards it as playing a vital role in health reform, putting clinicians at the heart of world-class commissioning and allowing groups of family doctors and community clinicians to develop better services for their local communities. Practice-based commissioners, working closely with PCTs and secondary care clinicians, lead work on deciding clinical outcomes. They also play a key role in providing PCTs with valuable feedback on provider performance.

Since 2005, GP practices have been able to hold an 'indicative' budget – money their PCT would otherwise control – to spend on secondary services. The intention is they will reflect their patients' preferences, leading to greater variety of services from a greater number of providers and more convenience for patients, as well as more efficient use of resources. Practices may combine together to commission services. PCTs continue to be legally responsible for contracting, but practices can keep up to 70 per cent of any savings to reinvest in premises, diagnostic or other equipment, patient services or staff.

The policy is designed to encourage GPs, nurses and other primary care professionals to translate patient needs into redesigned services that best deliver what local people want. It is also in line with the Government's overarching aims of devolving responsibility and increasing patient choice. Although practice-based commissioning remains voluntary, virtually all practices are now involved. A DH survey of practices in mid-2008 found 62 per cent in favour of practice-based commissioning and 15 per cent opposing it; 73 per cent had received an indicative budget from their PCT, but 66 per cent felt it had made little or no difference to how their practice operated. More than a fifth felt the relationship with their PCT was poor.

The Next Stage Review acknowledged 'a widespread view' that, with some exceptions, practice-based commissioning 'has not yet lived up to its potential'. It pledged to 'reinvigorate' it and 'give greater freedoms and support to high-performing GP practices'. The King's Fund concluded that practice-based commissioning had proved expensive and delivered little in terms of better services for patients or financial savings. Progress was slow and appeared to be stalling completely in some areas: few GPs were using it to commission new services despite having been paid almost £100 million in incentives. It recommended the Government fundamentally reassess the policy and tackle GPs' waning enthusiasm.

The DH has now created a practice-based commissioning development framework through which PCTs, SHAs and practice-based commissioners can call on help from five approved external organisations.

### Further information
*Practice-based commissioning: reinvigorate, replace or abandon?* King's Fund, November 2008.
*PBC development framework: an introduction*, DH, December 2008.
*Practice-based commissioning: GP practice survey waves 1–5 results (December 2008)*, DH, December 2008.
*Clinical commissioning: our vision for practice-based commissioning*, DH, March 2009.
www.practicebasedcommissioning.info

# Joint commissioning

The NHS and local government commission some services jointly. Indeed, the Government's planning framework (see page 116) treats health and social care as one system, with shared-lead priorities where both health and social care organisations have a major contribution to make. In Northern Ireland, health and social care have been combined since 1973. In Scotland, community health partnerships have increased coterminosity between NHS and local authority boundaries.

In all areas, joint working and engagement with local authorities are required – especially in tackling health inequalities, expanding intermediate care, implementing national service frameworks, improving services for vulnerable people and those with long-term conditions, as well as tackling neighbourhood renewal.

The white paper, *Our health, our care, our say*, noted that, 'People do not care about organisational boundaries when seeking support or help, and expect services to reflect this'. The Government is keen to see more co-location of health and social care services, and has promised to support the NHS and local government 'in developing more effective partnerships to fund and develop joint capital projects'. Other measures include:

- further development of local area agreements (see page 54)
- integration of health and social care planning cycles
- joint health and social care plans for people with long-term conditions
- a single complaints procedure across health and social care (see page 154)
- a national framework for NHS continuing care assessments
- strengthening the public health director's role to link it more closely with local authority overview and scrutiny committees (see page 160)
- national criteria on means-testing services and a commitment to extend personalised budgets and direct payments.

### Encouraging co-operation through legislation

Powers to enable health and local authority partners to work together more effectively were contained in Section 31 of the 1999 Health Act and came into force in 2000. These were reinforced by the Local Government and Public Involvement in Health Act 2007.

The Health Act 1999 created a duty of co-operation between NHS bodies and local authorities in England and Wales. It provides for them to develop together local strategies for improving health and healthcare, and allows them to make joint arrangements for commissioning or providing health and health-related services. Strategic health authorities, primary care trusts, social care, housing, transport, leisure and library services, community and many acute services can all be involved.

Specifically, the Act introduced flexibilities to enable NHS organisations and local authorities to set up:
• pooled funds – to be spent on agreed projects for designated services
• lead commissioning – they can agree to delegate commissioning of a service to one lead organisation
• integrated provision – combining staff, resources and management structures to integrate a service from managerial level to the front line.

PCTs have the key role in representing the NHS in developing partnerships. For this they are required to work flexibly.

The NHS and local government have clear, common aims, objectives and activity, much of which contributes to delivering NHS priorities. Involvement in planning and prioritising provides ways of engaging with local communities and the voluntary sector, and ensures stakeholders' involvement in NHS planning objectives.

The Children Act 2004 enhances the NHS's role in working with local partners to safeguard children. For example, NHS trusts and local authorities can pool their children's budgets. The Act set up the role of children's commissioner for England and established a statutory duty for all agencies working with children to co-operate.

**Further information**
*Delivering health and wellbeing in partnership: the crucial role of the new local performance framework*, CLG/DH, December 2007.
*Partnership working: the facts*, Primary Care Trust Network/NHS Confederation, 2007.

## Joint strategic needs assessment
Under the Local Government and Public Involvement in Health Act 2007, PCTs and local authorities must carry out a joint strategic needs assessment (JSNA) to provide a firm foundation for commissioning. The aim of a JSNA is to identify areas for priority action through local area agreements and to help commissioners – including practice-based commissioners – specify outcomes that encourage local innovation. It focuses on population – not individual – need, and is a tool to identify groups whose needs are not being met and whose healthcare is producing poor results.

The JSNA should:
- describe the local population's future health, care and well-being needs, and how services will meet them
- look ahead three to five years
- analyse data
- define where inequalities exist
- use local views and evidence of how effective or ineffective services are to shape investment and disinvestment
- define achievable improvements in health and well-being.

In practice, the JSNA is led by the directors of public health, adult social care and children's services, working closely with the directors of commissioning and finance. It examines all the factors that impact on health, including employment, education, housing and the environment.

**Further information**
*Guidance on joint strategic needs assessment*, DH, December 2007.
*Implementing joint strategic needs assessment: pitfalls, possibilities and progress*, Health Services Management Centre, University of Birmingham for Department of Health and Integrated Care Network, July 2008.

**Local area agreements**
Local area agreements (LAAs) aim to improve local public services by setting out the 'deal' between central and local government and its partners. They are based on the principle that developing services collectively is more effective than in isolation. Every area in England has had an LAA since March 2007. They cover one or more local authorities, and focus on a collection of goals across a range of services that relate to either national or local priorities. To set these priorities the local authority liaises with other organisations, which pool or align their budgets in order to achieve them. The Government Office for the Region handles the negotiations with the local authority and its partners, with regional public health directors representing health interests.

The LAA is then sent to ministers for approval. Proposed LAAs are sent to the Secretary of State for Health accompanied by the regional public health director's assessment of the health content and a view as to whether the LAA should be agreed. LAAs have a three-year focus and include up to 35 targets. They are structured around four key themes:
- children and young people
- safer and stronger communities

- healthier communities for older people
- economic development and the environment.

LAAs are a means of tackling major health and well-being issues, such as increasing levels of obesity, an ageing population, inability to work because of ill health and the increasing number of people reporting mental health problems.

From 2009, comprehensive area assessments will examine how well local services are working together to improve quality of life and provide value for money. For the first time, local public services will be held collectively to account. CAA will look across councils, health bodies, police forces, fire and rescue services and other bodies responsible for local public services that are increasingly expected to work in partnership. Other service or organisation-specific assessments will continue but try to avoid duplication. Conducted by the Audit Commission, CAA uses a joint assessment framework combining the perspectives of seven partner inspectorates.

**Further information**
*Creating strong, safe and prosperous communities – statutory guidance: draft for consultation*, Department of Communities and Local Government, November 2007.

## Public health

Public health is concerned with improving the population's health, rather than treating the diseases of individual patients. Safeguarding and enhancing public health is therefore an important objective of commissioning. The official definition of public health, devised by former Chief Medical Officer Sir Donald Acheson, is: 'the science and art of preventing disease, prolonging life, and promoting health through the organised efforts of society'. Many of the aims of public health can only be achieved through partnerships across government departments and between the Government, NHS, local authorities, the private and voluntary sectors. This is especially true for tackling inequalities in health, which is a top priority for the Government. Other major challenges include obesity, smoking, sexually transmitted diseases, alcohol and drug misuse and improving mental health.

Public health professionals monitor the health status of the community, identify health needs, develop programmes to reduce risk and screen for early disease, control communicable disease, promote health, plan and evaluate healthcare provision and manage and implement change.

**Health Profile of England 2008**

This annual collation of national and regional data presents a snapshot of public health and well-being and makes international comparisons. When last published in January 2009 by the DH it showed:

- life expectancy is increasing, and is now at its highest ever level
- deaths from suicides, cancer and circulatory diseases are declining
- infant mortality is at its lowest ever level
- numbers of people smoking and deaths attributable to it are decreasing
- levels of physical activity and fruit and vegetable consumption are improving
- rates of diabetes and chlamydia are rising
- obesity in adults and children is increasing
- death rates for chronic liver disease and cirrhosis have risen markedly
- death rates from traffic accidents are among the lowest in the EU
- prevalence of obesity in England is the highest in the EU.

Health profiles for every local authority in England were published in 2008 by the DH and Association of Public Health Observatories.
**www.healthprofiles.info**

## *Choosing health* – the public health white paper

*Choosing health*, published in 2004, is based on the principle that the NHS should improve health and prevent disease, not just provide treatment for those who are ill. The white paper encompasses the Government's view that people should make their own choices about their lifestyle, and consequently their health, but that these should be guided by good information and advice about the choices available. The NHS will help, support and encourage people to choose healthy lifestyles.

Principles behind this approach to public health are:
- informed choices – people want to be able to make their own decisions about choices that affect their health and to have good-quality information to help them do so
- personalisation – support has to be tailored to the realities of individual lives
- working together – progress depends on effective partnerships across communities.

The white paper pushed public health towards the top of priorities across government. It recognised the significant health benefits that could be gained by tackling public health issues, and it acknowledged – importantly – that the NHS could not solve all health-related problems on its own.

The DH has recently devised a plan to use social marketing to improve public health, basing targeted action on evidence of what motivates people to lead healthier lives. *Ambitions for health* focuses on:
- health capacity – increasing public health professionals' skills and knowledge through conferences, seminars and research materials
- health insight – a 'one-stop research shop' will collect useful data in one place
- health innovations – learning from the successes of programmes such as health trainers and life checks
- health partnerships – a £1 million a year fund to support partnerships.

**Further information**
*Choosing health: making healthier choices easier*, DH, November 2004.
*Delivering choosing health: making healthier choices easier*, DH, March 2005.
*Health Challenge England – next steps for choosing health*, DH, October 2006.
*Choosing health progress report*, DH, May 2007.
*Ambitions for health: a strategic framework for maximising the potential of social marketing and health-related behaviour*, DH, July 2008.

## Reducing health inequalities
Health inequalities start early in life, persist into old age and are repeated in subsequent generations. They exist in many forms. Different regions have different levels of health. Children born in lower socio-economic backgrounds are more likely to die at birth, suffer more illness throughout their life and die younger. Unemployment and poor housing, in particular, are significant causes of ill health. Ethnicity also plays a major role, with a higher prevalence of disease among different racial groups. Health inequality is found by gender, disability, sexual orientation and lifestyle. It is both avoidable and fundamentally unfair.

Action to break the cycle of deprivation and its impact on health is central to much Government policy. Tackling health inequalities and improving health require active commitment by government departments and groups at all levels – national, regional and local. Joint working, partnerships, networking, shared funding and resources are crucial.

## Spotlight on policy: Health Work Wellbeing

Health Work Wellbeing is a Government-led initiative to improve the health and well-being of working-age people. Founded on evidence that working is good for health, it brings together employers, unions and healthcare professionals to help more people with health conditions find and stay in employment. A cross-government programme, it was launched in 2005 by the DH, Department for Work and Pensions and the Health and Safety Executive. It now also includes the Scottish and Welsh Assembly governments. Its aim is 'to break the link between ill health and inactivity, to advance the prevention of ill health and injury, to encourage good management of occupational health, and to transform opportunities for people to recover from illness while at work'.

The strategy is led by a national director for health and work, Dame Carol Black, who found that ill health cost £100 billion a year and that access to good work-related health support was inadequate in the early stages of sickness, with provision disproportionately concentrated among a few large employers, leaving most without support. She proposed:
- piloting a Fit for Work service for patients in the early stages of illness
- if successful, the service to be extended to those on incapacity and other out-of-work benefits
- the traditional 'sick note' to be replaced by an electronic 'fit note' stating what people can do rather than what they cannot
- occupational health to be brought into the mainstream of healthcare provision.

The Government accepted most of the recommendations and intends to set up a National Centre for Working-Age Health and Wellbeing, introduce local co-ordinators to stimulate action, establish a fund for local initiatives and review the health and well-being of the NHS workforce.

### Further information
*Health, work and wellbeing – caring for our future: a strategy for the health and wellbeing of working age people*, DWP, DH & HSE, October 2005.
*Working for a healthier tomorrow*, TSO, March 2008.
*Improving health and work: changing lives – the Government's response to Dame Carol Black's review of the health of Britain's working-age population*, TSO, November 2008.
*Briefing 56: The healthy workplace agenda*, NHS Employers, December 2008.
www.workingforhealth.gov.uk

## Government action

Since 2004 the DH's public service agreement with the Treasury (see page 117) has contained a target to reduce inequalities in health outcomes by 10 per cent by 2010, as measured by infant mortality and life expectancy at birth. The life-expectancy element focuses on reducing the health gap between the fifth of local authority areas with the lowest life expectancy at birth and the rest of the population. The infant mortality aspect of the target seeks to reduce the gap between manual groups and the rest of the population.

In addition, other Government initiatives designed to reduce inequalities include:
- national minimum wage
- working families tax credit
- child tax credits
- minimum income guarantee for pensioners
- winter fuel payments
- the New Deal
- Sure Start.

A group of 'spearhead' PCTs covering 70 local authorities identified as the most health-deprived areas are piloting initiatives, such as health trainers and enhanced smoking-cessation services, to reduce health inequalities. Over a quarter of the population of England are included in the initiative.

The NHS at national level has also appointed a director for equality and human rights 'to tackle inequalities in all aspects of health and social care delivery'.

Although a DH progress report in 2008 found some improvements, it acknowledged that the health of the most disadvantaged people had not improved as quickly as that of the better off, and in some cases health inequalities had widened. In particular, smoking, drinking and obesity are major contributors to health inequalities, with people from lower socio-economic groups more susceptible to them.

Despite the 2010 target remaining very challenging, the Government reaffirmed its commitment to it and to further reducing health inequalities beyond then. It is scaling up work shown to be effective locally. Measures include:
• the national support team (NST) for health inequalities working with spearhead PCTs and sharing its approach with non-spearhead areas
• new NSTs for infant mortality and alcohol
• the NST for tobacco control concentrating on improving services for routine and manual workers.

The immediate focus is on actions that can change lives in the short term, although the full impact on health inequalities will take many years to show. Longer-term measures include:
• investing in early years and parenting
• tackling the poorer quality of service received by people with learning disabilities
• using employment to improve well-being and health
• promoting mental health and well-being.

The DH has commissioned a post-2010 strategic review of health inequalities by Professor Sir Michael Marmot, which will focus on the social determinants of health and in particular, the way they influence health inequalities. The review's final report is expected by the end of 2009.

## How the NHS can help reduce health inequalities

The NHS cannot tackle health inequalities alone. Housing, local authorities, employment agencies, the police and employers all have a major role to play. Such a complex problem has no simple national solution: every local area has within it many kinds of inequality with different underlying causes. But some aspects of health and healthcare either exacerbate inequalities or could be better used to narrow the inequality gap.

The NHS can help by:
- finding the millions of people who do not access services, through better disease mapping
- assisting people from poorer backgrounds to access services in the early stages of disease when cure or condition management is possible
- using its power as the UK's largest employer to offer equal opportunities in employment and encouraging local organisations to work together.

PCTs are responsible locally for leading partnerships and influencing partners so that their services help improve health and narrow health inequalities.

### Further information

*In sickness and in health: how the NHS can help tackle health inequalities*, NHS Confederation, December 2007.
*Health inequalities: progress and next steps*, DH, June 2008.
*Briefing 166: Health inequalities: progress and next steps*, NHS Confederation, July 2008.
*Are we choosing health? The impact of policy on the delivery of health improvement programmes and services*, Healthcare Commission/Audit Commission, July 2008.
*Tackling health inequalities: 2005–07 policy and data update for the 2010 national target*, DH, December 2008.
The Marmot review **www.ucl.ac.uk/gheg/marmotreview**

## Landmarks in tackling health inequalities

**1998** The Government-commissioned independent inquiry led by Sir Donald Acheson makes 40 recommendations on areas including poverty, income and ethnicity.

**1999** The white paper *Saving lives: our healthier nation* sets objectives to improve the whole nation's health and the health of the worst off. *Reducing health inequalities: an action report* is also published.

**2000** The NHS Plan commits the Government to setting national health inequality targets.

**2002** The comprehensive spending review contains a cross-cutting review on health inequalities.

**2003** The DH, with the support of 11 other government departments, publishes *Tackling health inequalities – a programme for action*, a three-year plan covering a range of local, regional and national organisations including the NHS, local authorities, social services, education, planning and employment.

**2004** The Wanless Report recommends radical changes in primary care, investments in workforce and a much more rigorous approach to tackling public health. The DH's public service agreement further raises the profile of tackling inequalities.

**2010** The target date by which the Government intends to reduce inequalities in health by 10 per cent.

## Public health workforce

The public health workforce comprises people in a range of disciplines who work in one of three categories:

- health improvement and reducing inequalities: teachers, local business leaders, managers, social workers, transport engineers, housing officers, other local government staff and the voluntary sector, as well as doctors, nurses and other healthcare professionals
- public health practice: health visitors, environmental health officers and community development workers, and those who use research, information, public health science or health promotion skills in specific public health fields
- public health consultants and specialists, who work at a strategic or senior management level or at a senior level of scientific expertise.

The public health system in England has ten core functions:
- health surveillance, monitoring and analysis
- investigation of disease outbreaks, epidemics and health risks

- establishing, designing and managing health promotion and disease prevention programmes
- enabling communities and citizens to promote health and reduce inequalities
- creating and sustaining cross-governmental and inter-sectoral partnerships to improve health and reduce inequalities
- ensuring compliance with regulations and laws to protect and promote health
- developing and maintaining a well-educated and trained, multi-disciplinary public health workforce
- ensuring the effective performance of NHS services to meet goals in improving health, preventing disease and reducing inequalities
- research, development, evaluation and innovation
- quality-assuring the public health function.

**Key organisation: Health Protection Agency**
The Health Protection Agency advises the Government on public health protection policies and programmes. It also supports the NHS and other agencies in protecting people from infectious diseases, poisons, chemical and radiological hazards. It provides a rapid response to health protection emergencies, including the deliberate release of biological, chemical, poison or radioactive substances. It merged with the National Radiological Protection Board in 2005 to form a UK-wide comprehensive health protection service. It has 3,000 staff based in three major centres and locally throughout England.
**www.hpa.org.uk**

**Key text: *Getting ahead of the curve: a strategy for combating infectious diseases***
This sets out an infectious diseases strategy for England and was published by the DH in 2002. The strategy describes the scope and nature of the threat posed by infectious diseases, and establishes priorities for action to combat present as well as possible future threats. Among these measures are a local health protection service, a strengthened and expanded system of surveillance, rationalisation of microbiology laboratories, a programme of new vaccine development and plans to combat the deliberate release of biological, chemical or radiological agents.

## Regional public health groups

When strategic health authorities were reorganised in 2006, their public health teams were combined with the DH's regional public health teams, which have been located in the nine Government Offices for the English Regions (GOs) since 2002.

The regional public health groups are charged with:
- developing a cross-government and cross-sector approach to tackling the wider determinants of ill health
- informing regional work on economic regeneration, education, employment and transport
- ensuring a proper health contribution to local strategic partnerships
- accountability for the protection of health (including against communicable diseases and environmental hazards) across the region
- making sure the public health function is properly managed locally
- emergency and disaster planning and management
- being the main point of contact for serious concerns about clinical standards and associated enquiries.

The nine GOs are: North East, North West, Yorkshire and the Humber, East Midlands, West Midlands, East of England, London, South East and South West.
www.gos.gov.uk/national

## Public health observatories

Public health observatories (PHOs) are closely linked to the regional public health groups. Their job is to support local bodies by:
- monitoring health and disease trends, highlighting areas for action
- identifying gaps in health information
- advising on methods for assessing the impact of health inequalities
- drawing together information on new ways to improve health
- carrying out projects to highlight particular health issues
- evaluating local agencies' progress in improving health and reducing inequality
- giving early warning of public health problems.

The 12 observatories are co-ordinated by the Association for Public Health Observatories and work across England, Scotland, Wales, Northern Ireland and the Republic of Ireland.
www.apho.org.uk

**Spotlight on policy: Preparing for a flu pandemic**

Influenza pandemics have occurred from time to time throughout history, so it is likely another will occur with little warning. It would have significant social and economic impact as well as a serious effect on the population's health. Previous pandemics have infected between 25 to 35 per cent of the population, and 20 million people died worldwide in the 1918 outbreak. A thorough and integrated response is therefore vital.

The Government has devised a national flu pandemic framework to co-ordinate responses from all departments, regional assemblies and public and private bodies if a pandemic occurs. The framework offers guidance to organisations on developing their plans. It includes information about decisions on school closures, international travel and public gathering, as well as outlining how people would get antiviral drugs through a national flu line service. A pandemic would pose a major operational challenge to the NHS and place great demands on staff.

The plans consider a 'reasonable worst case scenario' involving infection rates of 50 per cent. Counter-measures include:
• buying 33.5 million courses of antivirals to cover more than half the population
• buying 14.7 million courses of antibiotics to cover groups at risk
• ordering 350 million surgical masks and 34 million respirators for NHS and social care staff.

The DH has also contributed to a five-year cross-government international pandemic preparedness strategy, and donated £35 million since 2006 towards international activities to combat the threat of a flu pandemic. A World Health Organisation evaluation found the UK's plans to be among the world's most advanced.

**Further information**

*Pandemic flu: a national framework for responding to an influenza pandemic,* Cabinet Office/DH, November 2007.

*Pandemic flu: UK international preparedness strategy,* Cabinet Office/DH, October 2008.

**The smoking ban**

Smoking in enclosed public places was banned in England in July 2007, and in Wales and Northern Ireland in April 2007; it was banned in Scotland in March 2006. The ban follows similar decisions in other parts of Europe – the Irish Republic introduced a ban in 2004 – and the USA.

Anyone smoking in an enclosed public place may be fined £50, while those in charge of the premises may be fined £2,500. Failure to display no-smoking signs could lead to a £200 on-the-spot fine.

One year after the ban, compliance stood at 98 per cent; 76 per cent of people said they supported the ban – including 55 per cent of smokers. Local NHS stop-smoking services reported a 22 per cent increase in numbers quitting compared with a year earlier. It is estimated the ban will help prevent 40,000 deaths during the next ten years.

Between 1998 and 2008, the proportion of adult smokers in England fell from 28 to 21 per cent – a reduction of 1.2 million. But smoking still causes 106,000 deaths a year in the UK. After consulting on the future of tobacco control, the Government announced a ban on cigarette displays in shops from 2011 for larger stores and 2013 for smaller ones.

**Further information**

*Consultation on the future of tobacco control: consultation report*, DH, December 2008.
*Smokefree England – one year on*, DH, July 2008.

## Public health national support teams

Seven public health national support teams have been set up to give intensive support to areas struggling to meet *Choosing health* targets. They focus on:
• sexual health
• tobacco control
• health inequalities
• teenage pregnancy
• childhood obesity
• alcohol
• infant mortality.

Each draws expertise in clinical areas, service management, change management, commissioning and public health from the NHS, local government and the voluntary sector.

**Tackling climate change**

The potential impacts of climate change on health are many and varied. In the UK, hotter drier summers, milder wetter winters, more flooding and heat waves could mean:

- fewer cold-related winter deaths and more heat-related summer deaths
- more cases of food poisoning and insect-borne diseases
- more cases of sunburn and skin cancer.

The DH's priorities for coping with climate change are:

- adapting the health and social care infrastructure to cope with new demands
- ensuring national and local adaptation plans are implemented and evaluated
- raising awareness among public and professions of the health impacts.

It has issued guidance on tackling climate change and promoting sustainable communities that includes advice on:

- designing flood-resilient buildings that stay cool in summer, warm in winter
- reducing carbon footprints
- public awareness campaigns such as the 'Heatwave Plan'.

The NHS is responsible for over 18 million tonnes of carbon dioxide a year – 3.2 per cent of England's emissions – and for 25 per cent of public sector emissions. Its carbon reduction strategy commits the NHS to a 10 per cent reduction in its 2007 carbon footprint by 2015.

The NHS Sustainable Development Unit was set up in 2008 by the Office of the SHAs to:

- provide leadership, expertise and guidance on sustainable development
- promote a culture of measurement and management that underpins carbon governance
- help shape NHS policy locally, nationally and internationally
- evaluate and cost best practice and innovations on sustainability, helping the NHS with implementation.

**Further information**

*Health effects of climate change in the UK 2008: an update of the Department of Health report 2001/2002*, DH, February 2008.

*The health impact of climate change: promoting sustainable communities – guidance document*, DH, April 2008.

*Taking the long term view: the Department of Health's strategy for delivering sustainable development 2008–2011*, DH, October 2008.

*Saving carbon, improving health: NHS carbon reduction strategy for England*, NHS Sustainable Development Unit, January 2009.

NHS Sustainable Development Unit **www.sdu.nhs.uk**

# 03 Providing services

NHS organisations provide a wide range of services, outside hospitals and within them. Historically, hospitals have dominated the NHS's resources, but today much more care can be provided in GP surgeries and health centres closer to people's homes – and it is Government policy that it should be. It wants patients to have much more choice than hitherto over where they are treated, and it wants the services provided to feel more personal, taking greater account of people's preferences than was customary in the past.

## Primary care

Primary care is normally the patient's first point of consultation with the health service. It is concerned with promoting health as well as treating and managing conditions that do not require specialist care in hospital. For NHS patients, primary care provides the key to navigating the rest of the healthcare system: GPs, community nurses, health visitors, allied health professionals, pharmacists, dentists and opticians have a role as advocates for patients needing services from other parts of the NHS. Providing continuity of care is another important aspect.

About 90 per cent of NHS patients receive their treatment in primary care, and over 300 million consultations take place every year in England alone. The Next Stage Review stated: 'It is a central part of our strategy for primary and community care that we support the NHS and community clinicians in transforming these services and according them an equal status to other NHS services.' Advances, especially in diagnostics and minor surgery, mean many more treatments once carried out in hospital can be performed in primary care – a rapidly growing trend convenient for patients and of benefit to the system as a whole. Over 5 million people in England live more than ten miles from their nearest hospital.

A wide range of staff work in primary care in England. In 2007 there were:
- 35,855 GPs
- 22,860 practice nurses
- 94,515 practice staff, including practice managers, receptionists, IT support and notes summarisers, physiotherapists, podiatrists, counsellors, phlebotomists and healthcare assistants.

*NHS Next Stage Review: our vision for primary and community care*
As part of the Next Stage Review's final reports in July 2008, the
Government set out its plans for primary care over the next ten years,
emphasising that change will be driven by local choices and priorities
rather than top-down targets. Measures include:
- greater choice of GP, with patients able to register online and routinely consult their GP by phone or e-mail
- practice funding rewarding GPs who take on new patients to support greater patient choice
- faster and simpler access to community-based services for minor ailments, health checks in high street pharmacies and walk-in centres, and self-referral to physiotherapy or podiatry
- high-performing GPs given greater freedom to develop new services
- increasing access to 'healthy living services' such as exercise classes, stop-smoking support or help in managing stress
- identifying those most at risk of ill health and offering early interventions
- new programmes of clinical leadership, innovation and training.

### General practitioners

Most GP practices are independent contractors and are run as
partnerships, although some salaried GPs are employed by primary care
trusts, while specialist companies run some practices. GPs held on average
87 surgery and 17 telephone consultations a week in 2006/07, and made
five home visits. An average surgery consultation lasted 12 minutes, and
each phone consultation seven minutes.

Under the general medical services contract, all GP practices are required
to provide 'essential services': they must manage patients who are ill or
believe themselves to be ill, giving health promotion advice and making
referrals as necessary. They must also manage patients who are terminally
ill and those with chronic diseases. All practices are expected to provide
'additional services' such as contraception or childhood immunisations,
but they can opt out of them. They may also choose to provide 'enhanced
services' in response to need, such as minor surgery, specialised services
for patients with multiple sclerosis and specialised sexual health services.
The Quality and Outcomes Framework (see page 129) is designed to
maintain high standards and broaden the range of services GPs offer.

The Government is keen for GPs to widen their role to include services traditionally found only in hospitals. It believes that those with accredited specialist skills could handle more minor operations, while specially trained GPs and senior consultants should routinely work together in community hospitals and health centres. Operations for conditions such as cataracts, hernias and varicose veins could be done on the same site, reducing waiting times and potentially saving money. Other developments might include:

- GPs managing far more of their patients' social and health needs
- GPs, nurses and consultants forming 'day surgery companies'
- more GPs working from one-stop health centres, so patients can get follow-up treatment and tests in a single visit
- pharmacists taking on a wider role
- a voluntary GP accreditation scheme to reassure patients that their GP is meeting clinical standards.

Current initiatives are designed to improve patients' access to GP services (see page 48) and to give GPs more say over how NHS resources are spent through practice-based commissioning (see page 50).

**Further information**
*Keeping it personal – clinical case for change: report by David Colin-Thomé, national director for primary care*, DH, February 2007.

## Practitioners with a special interest
One way in which primary care services are expanding is by developing the role of practitioners with special interests.

GPs with a special interest (GPSIs) have additional training and expertise enabling them to provide a clinical service beyond the scope of normal general practice, undertake advanced procedures or develop services. They take referrals from colleagues for conditions in specialties such as ophthalmology, orthopaedics, dermatology and ear, nose and throat surgery, or undertake diagnostic procedures such as endoscopy. GPSIs do not offer a full consultant service, replace consultants or interfere with access to consultants by local GPs. Typically they undertake two sessions a week in their specialty.

GPSIs can increase the capacity of primary care to undertake outpatient appointments, reduce patient waiting times, provide a more convenient service and help to free consultant time in secondary care. Over 1,750 GPSIs are currently practising.

**Patient choice**

The Government wants the NHS to offer more convenient, 'personalised care' that takes account of patients' preferences concerning where and when they are treated. It also aims to develop a more market-based system for elective care, driven by patient choice. Since April 2008, all patients referred for an elective procedure are supposed to have had a 'free choice' of any hospital, clinic or treatment centre in England which meets NHS standards and price, including those in the independent sector. GPs may refer to any clinically appropriate provider, and PCT commissioning arrangements do not restrict where patients are offered a choice. Patients can also choose the date and time of their appointment.

Providers are listed in a national directory of services that is part of the Choose and Book facility on the NHS Choices website (see page 222), from which they can be booked directly. It claims to be 'the single most comprehensive, validated and easily searchable source of comparative data on the quality and availability of services'. It includes information on hospitals' MRSA rates, survival rates and car parking.

By early 2009, 28,000 bookings a day were made through Choose and Book. A DH survey in July 2008 found that 47 per cent of patients were aware before they visited their GP that they had a choice of hospitals for their first appointment, and 46 per cent recalled being offered a choice. Of these, 88 per cent were able to go to the hospital they wanted. Hospital cleanliness and low infection rates were selected most often as important when choosing a hospital.

The 2003 strategy paper, *Building on the best*, first outlined aspects of patient choice the Government wanted to see, and the introduction of free choice is the culmination of a six-year process. Introduction of choice has coincided with improvements in waiting times – although it remains controversial, with concerns about equity, the stability of NHS providers and a perceived threat to professional judgement. However, all political parties now endorse patient choice in principle, and to varying degrees in practice.

**Further information**

*Building on the best; choice, equity and responsiveness in the NHS*, DH, December 2003.
*Choice matters 2007–8: putting patients in control*, DH, June 2007.
NHS Choices **www.nhs.uk**
Choose and Book **www.chooseandbook.nhs.uk**

Initially, emphasis was on developing GPs with special interests, but dentists and pharmacists have now been included. Nurses and allied health professionals have developed their own approaches without adopting the terminology. A national accreditation framework for GPs and pharmacists with a special interest was launched in 2007 to ensure standards of care in the community are equivalent to those in acute care. PCTs have accreditation panels to verify GPs' and pharmacists' skills. Re-accreditation is carried out within three years.

Research has shown that while GPSI services improve access, they can be more costly than hospital clinics.

**Further information**
*Briefing paper: an assessment of the clinical effectiveness, cost and viability of NHS general practitioners with special interest (GPSI) services*, NHS SDO R&D Programme, September 2006.
*Implementing care closer to home – convenient quality care for patients*, DH, April 2007.

## Redesigning the fabric of primary care
The GP surgery is the focus of most primary care and the source of ever wider-ranging services. In 2000 the NHS Plan described a vision of the GP surgery of the future:

> Many GPs will be working in teams from modern multi-purpose premises alongside nurses, pharmacists, dentists, therapists, opticians, midwives and social care staff. Nurses will have new opportunities, and some GPs will tend to specialise in treating different conditions. The consulting room will become the place where appointments for outpatients and operations are booked, test results received and more diagnosis carried out using video and tele-links to hospital specialists. An increasing number of consultants will take outpatient sessions in local primary care centres.

Since then, PCTs have been encouraged to set up one-stop health centres – sometimes referred to as 'supersurgeries' or polyclinics – which bring services such as GPs, health visitors, dentists, a pharmacy, a cardiology clinic, x-ray facilities, optometry, Sure Start and a healthy living café under one roof. About 750 such centres have been built since 2001, and 3,000 other GP premises – about a third of the total – substantially refurbished or replaced. The Next Stage Review called for a further 150 'GP-led health centres' that would open from 8am to 8pm seven days a week.

In addition, walk-in centres provide fast access to advice and treatment for minor ailments and injuries without an appointment. There are about 90 throughout England, which see 3 million patients a year. They include seven instant-access GP-led centres for commuters commissioned from the independent sector. The first opened at Manchester Piccadilly Station in 2005.

Walk-in centres – also known as minor injury units or urgent care centres – are open seven days a week, from 7am to 10pm, and offer assessment by an experienced NHS nurse as well as information on out-of-hours GP, dental and local pharmacy services. The centres are helping improve access for groups with particular needs, including young or homeless people. An established walk-in centre sees around 2,500 patients per month.

The Government has made available £750 million over five years to develop 'a new generation of modern NHS community hospitals' by refurbishing outdated ones and building new ones. These are not like-for-like replacements but, as with GP-led health centres and walk-in centres, offer new means of delivering primary care. Their focus varies but may include minor injuries, diagnostic and screening services, minor surgery and outpatient clinics. Some offer intermediate care or rehabilitation services. Some are staffed exclusively by nurses supported by local GPs, others by hospital outreach services.

**Further information**
*Ideas from Darzi: polyclinics*, NHS Confederation, April 2008.
Community Hospitals Association **www.communityhospitals.org.uk**

## Dental services
Most dentists in primary care are self-employed and contract their services to PCTs, like most GPs. They numbered 20,815 in 2008. By 2010, 25 per cent more dental graduates will begin NHS training. A fourfold increase to 200 training places for dental therapists is also underway.

Policy on dental services lagged behind other health sectors until 2006, when over 400 charges for treatment were replaced by three standard charges for all treatments and the £1.9 billion budget for primary care dental services was devolved to PCTs. This covers surgery salaries and expenses instead of the piecework pay system set up when the NHS was founded. Access to dentistry has been a high-profile issue for more than 15 years, with increasing concerns about gaps in access to NHS-funded services and many practices opting out or closing to new NHS patients. Surgeries have therefore been encouraged to broaden their range of services. The intention is that dentists can focus on prevention and health promotion, as well as treatment within their NHS contracts, and spend more time with patients.

The Government has acknowledged that the transition period proved difficult for PCTs and dentists, with a 3 per cent fall in the number of patients seen. It increased funding for dentistry by 11 per cent in 2008/09 so that PCTs could commission a wider range of services.

Nevertheless, access remains a problem in parts of the country. The Government has therefore launched an independent review of NHS dentistry, which will examine access and other issues raised by the Commons health committee. It will report during 2009.

**Further information**
*NHS dental reforms: one year on*, DH, August 2007.
*Dental services: fifth report of session 2007–08*, House of Commons health committee, June 2008.
*Government response to the Health Select Committee report on dental services*, TSO, October 2008.

## Community pharmacies
Britain's 10,000 high street pharmacies are visited by 6 million people every day and employ 73 per cent of pharmacists. They increasingly offer services traditionally available only at GPs' surgeries. The pharmacy contract introduced in 2005 aims to improve the range and quality of services of the community pharmacy and integrate it more into the NHS. It defines three tiers of service:
- Essential services must be provided by all community pharmacists. They include dispensing, disposal of medication and support for self-care.
- Advanced services require the pharmacist to have accreditation and/or their premises to meet certain standards. So far, medicines use review and prescription intervention fall in this category.
- Enhanced services are commissioned locally by PCTs. Examples include minor ailment schemes and smoking-cessation services.

Many pharmacies now offer new services such as:
- repeat prescribing, so that patients can get up to a year's supply of medicines without having to revisit their GP

- clinics for people with conditions such as diabetes, high blood pressure or high cholesterol
- signposting other health and social care services and supporting self-care
- consultation areas.

The DH white paper, *Pharmacy in England*, included proposals for pharmacies to:
- be able to prescribe common medicines and be the first port of call for minor ailments – saving every GP an hour a day and totalling 57 million GP consultations a year
- support people with long-term conditions, half of whom may not take their medicines as intended
- screen for vascular disease and certain sexually transmitted infections
- play a bigger role in vaccination.

**Further information**
*The new contractual framework for community pharmacy*, DH, October 2004.
*Review of progress on reforms to the 'control of entry' system for NHS pharmaceutical contractors – report*, DH, January 2007.
*Pharmacy in England: building on strengths, delivering the future*, DH, April 2008.
*Briefing 160: Pharmacy in England*, PCTN/NHS Confederation, May 2008.

## Opticians
There are three kinds of registered optician:

**Optometrists – or ophthalmic opticians** – carry out eye tests, look for signs of eye disease and prescribe and fit glasses and contact lenses. They are graduates who have undertaken a three- or four-year degree in optometry, then spent at least a year in supervised practice before taking professional exams leading to registration with the General Optical Council. There are about 10,000 registered optometrists in the UK.

**Dispensing opticians** fit and sell glasses, and interpret prescriptions, but do not test eyes. Some dispense low-vision aids, and some are qualified to fit contact lenses under instruction from an optometrist.

**Ophthalmic medical practitioners** are doctors specialising in eyes and eye care. They work to the same terms of service as optometrists.

In addition, **ophthalmologists** are doctors specialising in eye diseases and most perform eye surgery. They usually work in hospital eye departments.

**Orthoptists** treat disorders of binocular vision, and work in eye departments under the supervision of ophthalmologists. They may also undertake visual screening of children in the community.

Optometrists are independent contractors. Some have specialist skills – for example, in contact lenses, low vision or paediatrics – and can treat patients who would otherwise have to be seen in hospital. Most practices have much of the equipment found in ophthalmology clinics.

Under co-management, or shared care, optometrists working to an agreed protocol undertake specified clinical procedures designed to relieve GPs and the hospital eye service, as well as move patient care into the community. This may cover conditions such as glaucoma, diabetes, cataracts and minor acute eye problems. Throughout the UK, optometrists can now prescribe medicines for conditions of the eye and surrounding tissue if they are registered to do so with the General Optical Council and have undertaken special training.

PCTs are responsible for managing optometrists' contracts. Some employ optometric advisers to provide guidance on issues such as service development, new techniques and treatments, interpreting regulations, investigating complaints and audit.

The recent general optical service review assessed how eye-care services are currently provided and found potential for eye-care professionals in primary care to work alongside hospitals in developing more responsive services for patients with eye conditions such as glaucoma. It also identified scope for greater collaboration between the NHS, social care and the third sector in providing integrated services for patients with low-vision problems and in taking wider action to improve eye health.

**Further information**
*General ophthalmic services review: findings in relation to the framework for primary ophthalmic services, the position of dispensing opticians in relation to the NHS, local optical committees, and the administration of General Ophthalmic Services payments,*
DH, January 2007.

## Community health services

The Next Stage Review declared that it wanted to see 'vibrant, successful' community health services that are 'flexible, responsive'. Its report said: 'The 250,000 nurses, health visitors, allied health professionals and other staff working in our community health services have a crucial role to play in providing personal care, particularly for children and families, older people, those with complex care needs and those at the end of life. They are also central to our drive for promoting health and well-being and reducing health inequalities.'

A range of services are provided in the community by a variety of staff and organisations.

**Allied health professionals** – AHPs number over 76,000 and include art therapists, drama therapists, music therapists, chiropodists/podiatrists, dietitians, occupational therapists, orthoptists, orthotists and prosthetists, paramedics, physiotherapists, diagnostic radiographers, therapeutic radiographers and speech and language therapists. The DH has recently given AHPs the power to accept patients who refer themselves to AHP services.

**Community nurses** – who include district nurses with a postgraduate qualification, registered nurses and nursing assistants. More than half the patients they see will be aged over 75. About half their work comes from GP referrals and a quarter from hospital staff; patients and carers can also refer themselves.

**Community matrons** – as experienced nurses, community matrons use case management techniques with patients who make intensive use of healthcare to help them remain at home longer.

**Health visitors** – who are qualified nurses or midwives with additional training and experience in child health, health promotion and education. Much of their work is with mothers and babies using a child-centred, family-focused approach, although they do provide more general health advice to people of all ages. Their support staff include nursery nurses and healthcare assistants, who focus on less complex family support and parenting skills. A review of the health visitor's role in 2007 recommended they concentrate on leading a renewed child health promotion programme and on intensive early intervention and prevention for families who need help most.

**Specialist nurses** – with expertise in stoma care, continence services, palliative care and support for people with long-term conditions.

**School nursing** – providing support and advice to schools on health issues, a role which has evolved considerably in recent years.

**Community dentistry and dental public health** – providing services to schools and people who are difficult to treat.

**Podiatry** – foot care for elderly people or those with diabetes, gait or lower limb problems. Independent contractors provide much of this care. More than half the service is for people aged over 65.

**Physiotherapy** – sometimes provided by GPs or hospitals in a community setting, with emphasis on rehabilitation.

**Occupational therapy** – providing advice, aids and adaptations. Some staff specialise in adults, some in children. The service is often provided by other agencies, such as local government, although in some cases the NHS provides local authority OT services.

**Speech and language therapy** – services for children and adults who have difficulty with communicating, eating, drinking or swallowing.

**Clinical psychology** – often provided by specialist mental health trusts, although more than 40 per cent of referrals come from general practice.

**Midwives** – generally attached to hospitals, but working in community settings.

**Family planning services** – may cover sexual health problems as well as contraception, vasectomy and termination clinics and specialist clinics for young people.

**Community rehabilitation** – often for stroke or cardiac conditions. Services may be delivered by specialist teams in the patient's home or by combining intermediate care (see page 84) or community hospital care with home care.

The DH and Department for Children, Schools and Families have published a joint strategy for children's health. It sets out what children and their families can expect from child health services from birth to the age of 19. The strategy promises:

- stronger and better joined-up support during the early years of life, including more health visitors
- a strengthened role for Sure Start children's centres with each having access to a named health visitor
- expansion of the family nurse partnerships programme to support first-time mothers from 30 to 70 sites by 2011, with a view to extending it nationwide over the next decade
- an antenatal programme and preparation-for-parenthood package for mothers and fathers
- free school meal pilots looking at the health and educational benefits of universal access
- £340 million to support children with disabilities and their families.

**Further information**

*Healthy lives, brighter futures: the strategy for children and young people's health,* DH/DCSF, February 2009.

## Integrated care

According to the Next Stage Review: 'Integrated care means GPs, community nurses, pharmacists, social care teams, ambulance services, schools and others coming together on a collaborative basis with clear leadership, shared goals and shared information – and designing services around the needs of individuals and local communities.'

Integration is especially important for continuing care, long-term care, intermediate care and end-of-life care, which – to be effective – all depend on a high degree of co-ordination between different organisations providing health and social care. Integration might involve bringing together different kinds of expertise and interventions – for example, by creating teams of primary and secondary care clinicians, or health and social care professionals. Better integration could potentially support key Government objectives such as more personalised services and greater emphasis on health promotion and prevention.

## Integrated care pilot programme

The DH has launched a programme for PCTs to test ways of commissioning 'integrated care organisations' – multi-professional groups based around groups of GP practices. The pilots will run for two years and be evaluated over three years on criteria such as health outcomes, improved quality of care, patient satisfaction and effective relationships and systems.

About 20 final pilots will be selected during 2009 from 108 applications in the ten SHA regions. They cover long-term care, urgent care, care of the elderly, mental health and diabetes, and involve partnerships between primary care, social care, secondary care, the voluntary and private sectors.

### Further information

*Delivering care closer to home: meeting the challenge*, DH, July 2008.
*Integrated care pilot programme: prospectus for potential pilots*, DH, October 2008.

## Continuing care

Continuing care is care provided over an extended period to someone aged 18 or over to meet physical and mental health needs that have arisen as a result of disability, accident or illness. The person may require services from the NHS and/or local authorities. Where they are assessed as having mainly health needs, the NHS will arrange and fund the complete package, which may be provided in any setting – hospital, hospice, home or care home. If they live in a care home, the NHS will contribute to their registered nursing care. Financial issues are not taken into account when deciding eligibility for NHS continuing care. If a person does not qualify, the NHS may still have responsibility for contributing to a 'joint package' to meet their health needs.

The DH implemented a national framework for NHS continuing healthcare in 2007 in order to clarify eligibility criteria that had become increasingly confused.

### Further information

*The national framework for NHS continuing healthcare and NHS-funded nursing care*, DH, June 2007.
*Briefing 149: The national framework for NHS continuing healthcare and NHS-funded nursing care*, NHS Confederation, September 2007.

## Care for long-term conditions

More than 17.5 million people in the UK (15.4 million in England) suffer a long-term or chronic condition such as diabetes, asthma or arthritis. Best practice requires early recognition, prompt diagnosis and treatment, early and specialist rehabilitation, equipment and accommodation and support for family and carers. To ensure best quality care – and to maximise service efficiency – it is important that long-term conditions are effectively managed outside hospital wherever possible.

Health and social care organisations should assign community matrons to the most vulnerable patients with complex multiple long-term conditions, to monitor their condition, anticipate any problems and co-ordinate their care. Multi-professional teams should identify all people with a single serious long-term illness, assess their needs as early as possible and provide proactive care before their condition deteriorates. Everyone with a long-term condition should be educated about their health and encouraged to manage their own care more effectively. The Next Stage Review called for everyone with a long-term condition to have a personalised care plan and those with complex health needs to have a care co-ordinator by 2010.

### Further information

*Supporting people with long-term conditions. An NHS and social care model to support local innovation and integration*, DH, January 2005.

*National Service Framework for long-term conditions*, DH, March 2005.

*Your health, your way – a guide to long term conditions and self care (the 'Patients' Prospectus')*, DH, November 2008.

*Supporting people with long-term conditions: commissioning personalised care planning*, DH, January 2009.

The Long Term Conditions (LTC) Community **www.ltc-community.org.uk**

### Self-care

The DH has devised seven core principles of self-care to help health and social care staff support people with long-term conditions or complex needs to live independently and stay healthy. They are:

- ensure people can make informed choices to manage their self-care needs
- communicate effectively to enable people to assess their needs and gain confidence to care for themselves
- support and enable people to access appropriate information to manage their self-care

**Key organisation: Expert Patient Programme CIC**

A 2001 DH policy document, *The expert patient*, defined a new relationship between patient and professional, in which 'the era of the patient as the passive recipient of healthcare is changing and being replaced by a new emphasis on the relationship between the NHS and the people whom it serves'. Since then, over 30,000 people have attended an 'expert patients programme' in England. The EPP is a six-week course for people with chronic or long-term conditions that aims to give them the confidence to self-manage their health, while encouraging them to collaborate with health and social care professionals. Topics include healthy eating, dealing with pain and extreme tiredness, relaxation techniques and coping with feelings of depression.

Since 2007 the Expert Patients Programme has been a community interest company (CIC) with the purpose of expanding course places from 12,000 a year to over 100,000 by 2012.

While it has been a successful programme, EPP has been criticised for offering only a generic course rather than disease-specific training, which can be equally or more effective.

www.expertpatients.nhs.uk

• support and enable individuals to develop skills in self-care
• support and enable individuals to use technology for self-care
• advise individuals how to access support networks and participate in planning, developing and evaluating services
• support and enable risk management and risk-taking to maximise independence and choice.

**Further information**
*Self care: a national view in 2007 compared to 2004–05, DH, June 2007.*

## Intermediate care

Intermediate care is a vital component of the programme to improve the health and well-being of older people and raise the quality of their services. Older people are the main users of the NHS: although they make up about a fifth of the population, they occupy two-thirds of hospital beds, and are three times more likely to be admitted to hospital.

**Reforming care and support**

'Care and support' describes the activities, services and relationships that help people who are disabled or who have long-term conditions, are elderly or have suffered an accident to remain independent, active and healthy. With care and support costs set to double by 2026 due to a rapidly ageing population, the Government launched a six-month nationwide debate in 2008 on the future shape of services. It intends to publish a green paper in 2009. The challenge is the need to balance individual choice with available funding.

The Government has also set up a £31 million, two-year 'whole-system demonstrator programme' based at three sites to test the potential of technologies such as telecare and telehealth in supporting people with complex health and social care needs, such as those with diabetes, heart and chest problems, as well as the elderly and frail. Telecare is the continuous, automatic and remote monitoring of emergencies and lifestyle changes in order to manage the risks associated with independent living. Telehealth is healthcare provided at a distance using electronic communication. Expected benefits are fewer emergency admissions, less use of acute hospitals and reduced dependence on care homes.

**Further information**
*The case for change – why England needs a new care and support system*, HM Government, May 2008.
www.careandsupport.direct.gov.uk

Intermediate care comprises services to promote faster recovery, prevent unnecessary hospital admission, support timely hospital discharge and maximise a patient's ability to live independently. These services may include:
• rapid-response teams
• hospital-at-home schemes
• supported-discharge teams
• nurse-led facilities in acute or community settings
• council-run or independent residential rehabilitation.

By its nature, intermediate care is not the preserve of any single profession, organisation or sector. It includes health and social care as well as housing, and relies on partnerships between organisations and professions: health and social care jointly fund 5,000 intermediate care beds. It has developed enormously in recent years and is on the brink of being recognised as a mainstream service. But as its origins pre-date now established policy directions, intermediate care has evolved in many parts of the country through locally led initiatives in response to local service pressures. This has produced a wide diversity of models.

## End-of-life care

Half a million people die in England each year, three-quarters after a chronic illness. Surveys show most people would prefer to die at home, although only 18 per cent do so; 58 per cent die in hospital, 17 per cent in care homes, 4 per cent in a hospice and 3 per cent elsewhere. End-of-life care is becoming more complex, with people living longer and the incidence of frailty and multiple conditions in older people rising. The Government has therefore launched a ten-year end-of-life care strategy to help more people to die in the setting they choose, promote dignity and respect, properly co-ordinate services and support carers. It will be implemented with £286 million of extra resources between 2009 and 2011.

It will focus on:
- improved community services, ensuring rapid-response community nursing services are available everywhere around the clock
- workforce training and development in assessing patients' and carers' needs and providing best-quality care
- developing specialist palliative care outreach services in the community, to support all adults regardless of their condition
- setting up a national end-of-life research initiative on how best to care for those at the end of their lives
- quality standards against which PCTs and providers can assess themselves and be assessed by regulators.

### Further information
*End of life care strategy – promoting high quality care for all adults at the end of life,* DH, July 2008.
*End of life care, National Audit Office,* November 2008.

**Personal health budgets**

Personal (or individual) health budgets are designed to enhance independence and choice for people receiving care or support. A personal budget brings together resources from different funding streams into a single sum. The purpose is to give people a clear idea of the finance available and enable them to make their own decisions about their care – for example, by having someone support them at home rather than going into residential care. Pilots, recommended in the Next Stage Review, will begin at the end of 2009 and run until 2012.

A pilot programme for social care personal budgets, led by the DH working with the Department for Work and Pensions and the Department of Communities and Local Government, was conducted from 2006 to 2007, involving 13 local authorities. Those receiving budgets included older people, people with learning disabilities, physical disabilities and/or sensory impairments and mental health service users. They were supported by their care manager, broker, advocate, family or friends to plan what they wanted and how to organise it. The pilot found budgets particularly benefited mental health service users and younger disabled people.

Concerns remain that NHS money could be spent on treatments that are not cost-effective, such as expensive medication or alternative therapies. The impact of personal budgets on equity, funding and commissioning will need to be carefully assessed. The social care pilot programme found the impact on individuals varied: satisfaction was lowest among older people, who found planning and managing their own support burdensome.

**Further information**
*Evaluation of the individual budgets pilot programme: final report*, Individual Budgets Evaluation Network (IBSEN), October 2008.
*Personal health budgets: first steps*, DH, January 2009.
*Personal health budgets: the shape of things to come?* NHS Confederation, January 2009.

# Secondary care

## The changing role of hospitals

Acute hospitals have always dominated healthcare spending and provision, but their role has begun to change fundamentally. The Next Stage Review noted: 'The potential to use community settings for some services traditionally provided in hospitals – and in a way that really shifts the emphasis to supporting health and well-being rather than simply curing disease – is set to grow faster in the coming years as a result of demographic, economic and technological changes.' It added: 'We want to see more services available to people in their local communities or in their own homes to avoid unnecessary trips to hospitals (e.g. for outpatient appointments or diagnostic tests) and to make services more personal and effective.'

Changes in the last two decades have revolutionised surgery: lasers and 'keyhole' techniques have led to quicker recovery and less risk of infection. Procedures that previously required long stays in hospital, such as hernia operations, can now be done as day cases more locally. New drugs have made some surgery, such as treatment for stomach ulcers, completely unnecessary. The national adviser on surgery – now the Health Minister, Lord Darzi – has recommended that 80 per cent of all surgery should be done locally and the most complex 20 per cent take place at specialist centres with the most highly skilled surgeons using the latest technology.

Meanwhile, patient choice, payment by results and practice-based commissioning will shift the balance of power between organisations, stimulating further change – especially as value for money will become ever more important with the slowdown in spending.

The DH is working with six specialties in 30 demonstration sites to develop models of providing care 'closer to home'. The specialties are:
• ear, nose and throat
• trauma and orthopaedics
• dermatology
• urology
• gynaecology
• general surgery.

Vital statistics: average length of hospital stay – general and acute (days)

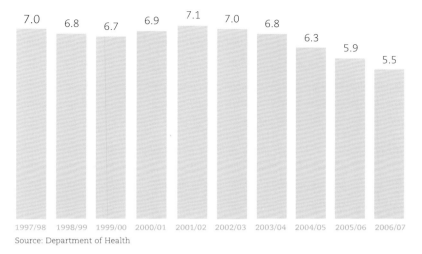

| 7.0 | 6.8 | 6.7 | 6.9 | 7.1 | 7.0 | 6.8 | 6.3 | 5.9 | 5.5 |
| 1997/98 | 1998/99 | 1999/00 | 2000/01 | 2001/02 | 2002/03 | 2003/04 | 2004/05 | 2005/06 | 2006/07 |

Source: Department of Health

The DH's National Clinical Advisory Team provides a pool of clinical experts to guide the local NHS on service change proposals to ensure they are safe and accessible for patients.

The result of these developments is that the traditional model of the district general hospital is changing. Local hospitals are likely to remain important, but rather than working in isolation will have to work much more in collaboration with other providers and each other as part of 'multi-hospital networks of care'. Rather than exercising local monopolies, hospitals will need to promote competition and choice.

Change to local health services is often controversial for staff and the public, who need to be involved in developing plans from early on. The Next Stage Review emphasised that any major change in hospital services should be clinically led, locally accountable and initiated only when a clear and strong clinical basis exists. Consultation should take place only where there is effective and early engagement with the public, and resources should be made available to open new facilities alongside old ones closing.

**Key organisation: Independent Reconfiguration Panel**

Set up in 2003, the IRP advises the Secretary of State on proposals for changes to NHS services that have been contested locally. It also offers advice to the NHS, local authorities and others on NHS reconfiguration issues.

The local authority overview and scrutiny committee (see page 160) may refer a proposal if it is not satisfied:
• with the content of the consultation or the time allowed
• with the reasons given for not carrying out consultation
• that the proposal is in the interests of the health service locally.

Although the IRP is a last resort when other options for local resolution have been explored, it welcomes early informal contact to avoid formal referral if possible. Once a case is accepted, the chair agrees any specific terms of reference and a timetable for reporting. The chair will normally appoint a sub-group of three (one health professional, one health manager, one patient and citizen representative) to consider the case. The IRP encourages locally acceptable solutions. Its advice takes account of public and patient involvement and the rigour of local consultation. As a non-departmental public body, the IRP offers advice only: final decisions rest with the Secretary of State.

**Further information**
*Learning from reviews: an overview*, IRP, November 2008.
www.irpanel.org.uk

The review also recommended that any proposals to change services should be subject to independent clinical and management assessment before consultation. Since 2008 this has been conducted under the Office of Government Commerce's gateway review process. It comprises a series of short reviews carried out at key stages and designed to highlight risks which could threaten a project's success. The review usually takes three to four days and involves interviewing clinicians, patients, users, boards, staff and managers.

DH guidance on major change to NHS services consists of 15 recommendations intended to ensure the process is open, transparent and fair. They include provisions that:

- each SHA should oversee proposals
- PCTs should normally lead the proposal's preparation and consultation
- proposals should be specific about their impact on the quality of patient services, including number of lives saved and reduction in health inequalities
- a senior clinical lead should be identified at the outset and helped to involve other clinicians
- chairs, chief executives and boards are accountable for and should take a personal lead in the proposals
- stakeholders should be involved throughout.

**Further information**
*The future of acute care, Andy Black*, NHS Confederation, January 2006.
*Saws and scalpels to lasers and robots: advances in surgery – clinical case for change; report by Sir Ara Darzi, national adviser on surgery*, DH, April 2007.
*Changing for the better: guidance when undertaking major changes to NHS services*, DH, May 2008.
*Delivering care closer to home: meeting the challenge*, DH, July 2008.
*Local hospitals: lessons for the NHS – Central Middlesex Hospital case study*, NHS Confederation, January 2009.

**Treatment centres**
Treatment centres are units that carry out planned surgery and treatment in areas that have traditionally had the longest waiting times, separating them from unplanned care and so lessening the risk that operations have to be cancelled. The Government has looked to them to create innovation, increase productivity and rapidly expand capacity. The aim has also been to create a plurality of providers to generate competition for patients. They have developed new staff roles, including perioperative specialist practitioners, advanced nurse practitioners/advisers and healthcare assistant technicians in radiology, ophthalmology and surgery.

A treatment centre's essential features include:
- delivering a high volume of routine treatments and/or diagnostics
- streamlined services using defined pathways
- planned and booked services, with emphasis on patient choice and convenience.

Treatment centres have developed on two models. Some are run by the NHS, others by the independent sector under contract to the NHS. They may be:

- virtual treatment centres – defined services within an existing hospital, using care pathways to ensure efficiency and enhance the patient's experience
- stand-alone new-build treatment centres – purposely designed for maximum efficiency and to ensure the best patient flows
- refurbished sites – possibly using surplus estate to give quick access to suitable buildings.

The type of work they do falls into three categories:

- short-stay inpatient work, often in a single specialty such as orthopaedics or ophthalmology
- day-case or outpatient work, sometimes referred to as 'surgi-centres'
- community-based diagnostic work, such as endoscopy and ultrasound, and minor surgical procedures such as excision of cysts and lesions, and vasectomies.

Centres may serve patients from a limited catchment area or accept those waiting a long time from anywhere. They may care for patients within a single specialty or a range of specialties.

Although TCs enable the NHS to treat patients more quickly than before, there are concerns that they could cause problems for some hospitals by removing large amounts of their work, so threatening the viability of some services. Several independent sector TCs have not performed as many operations as planned, and – in some cases – were already paid for: ISTCs that opened during the first phase were guaranteed payment irrespective of how many procedures they carried out. In the second phase, ISTCs were not guaranteed payment and initial plans were scaled down. A planned third phase was cancelled. Now PCTs are expected to decide for themselves about introducing a TC where they need to increase capacity or contestability.

### Further information

*Treatment centres: delivering faster, quality care and choice for NHS patients*, DH, January 2005.

NHS rules have always prohibited patients from supplementing their treatment by paying for additional care or medication. DH guidance stated: 'A patient cannot be both a private and an NHS patient for the treatment of one condition during a single visit to an NHS organisation'.

These rules have been challenged by cancer patients wishing to buy drugs unapproved by NICE (see page 158), who would be denied the rest of their NHS treatment as a result. Some new drugs – particularly for cancer – can be effective for certain people, extending life by months, but fail cost-effectiveness tests that NICE and PCTs apply. Government and PCTs have argued that allowing patients to 'top up' their treatment would undermine NHS principles of equity. Patients affected may be few at present but trends indicate they will increase.

Concerns arose that the top-up rule was being applied inconsistently, with trusts threatening or enforcing it in places, while others surrendered to pressure or reversed earlier decisions after individual campaigns. Some felt public and private funding were already blurred where, for example, a patient paid for private tests to reduce waiting time for surgery. It was argued that denying treatment to those topping up undermined the principle that everyone should have equal access to NHS services according to need.

Yet having two patients with similar needs receiving different levels of treatment could also contravene the principle of equity of access. A longer-term concern is that topping up would lead to a two-tier NHS, with a basic core package supplemented with a system of co-payments or means-testing for 'high-quality' care.

After a review, the Government has now instructed the NHS not to withdraw treatment from patients who pay privately for additional drugs, although private treatment should take place in a private facility and must not be subsidised by the NHS. In addition, the Government is to substantially widen access to drugs on the NHS and reduce the need for patients to resort to private treatment. NICE has devised a new system for appraising expensive drugs designed to help those with severe illness, and is speeding up its appraisal process.

Concerns remain about implementation of the review recommendations, including the impact of widening access to end-of-life drugs on the availability of other more effective treatments, the practicality for hospitals of physically separate private care and the effect on foundation trusts, which are limited in the number of private patients they can treat.

**Further information**

*Futures debate paper 4: Topping up – should it be allowed on the NHS?* NHS Confederation, June 2008.
*Improving access to medicines for NHS patients: a report for the Secretary of State for Health by Professor Mike Richards CBE*, COI, November 2008.
*Guidance on NHS patients who wish to pay for additional private care – a consultation*, DH, November 2008.

## Managed clinical networks

Clinical networks, first developed in Scotland (see page 235) are not statutory bodies but partnerships of all organisations and professionals involved in commissioning, planning and providing a particular service in a geographical area. They form, in effect, virtual organisations, and have the potential to break down barriers between primary, secondary and tertiary care and between health and social care. Good working relationships are crucial to their success, and they need multi-disciplinary leadership and management.

Networks help ensure all staff with whom a patient has contact are working to the same protocols and policies – for example, on admission, discharge and transfer: this can ease bed shortages and reduce the need for transferring patients between facilities. By collecting all information relevant to a clinical condition they enable network-wide audit to inform practice and future service developments. They encourage staff to work as one on common issues, and share learning although such collaboration has to be balanced with the DH's rules on competition (see page 44).

Networks are now well developed in cancer care, bringing together commissioners and providers, the voluntary sector and local authorities. There are currently 34 cancer care networks in the UK, each serving 1 to 2 million people.

## Urgent and emergency care

The system for delivering urgent and emergency care includes:

- NHS Direct
- community pharmacy and self-care (see pages 76 and 83)
- GP services, including out-of-hours services (see page 71)
- urgent care centres, including walk-in centres and minor injuries units (see page 75)
- ambulance services
- hospital accident and emergency departments
- critical care services.

Emergency care has been undergoing major changes since the launch of a ten-year strategy, Reforming Emergency Care, in 2001. The strategy is based on six key principles:

- services should be designed from the patient's point of view
- patients should receive a consistent response wherever, whenever and however they contact the service
- patients' needs should be met by the professional best able to help them
- information from each stage of the patient's journey should be shared with other professionals involved in their care
- assessment or treatment should not be delayed through the absence of diagnostic or specialist advice
- clear and measurable standards should be applied to emergency care.

The strategy aims to transform the patient's experience of emergency care through:

- shorter waits – no patient should spend more than four hours from arrival in A&E to admission, transfer or discharge
- faster ambulance response times and better training and equipment for crews
- more streamlined access, including more primary care-based services for minor complaints
- a more integrated approach to emergency and critical care.

The Next Stage Review kept up the pressure for further reform, noting that many people found it difficult to understand what services were available where and when. As a result, the DH is exploring the feasibility of introducing a three-digit telephone number for access to all urgent care services. The Healthcare Commission found 'significant improvements' in emergency and urgent care had been achieved in recent years as a result of new services such as NHS Direct and walk-in centres, faster ambulance response times and shorter waits in A&E. This was despite an increase in numbers using A&E and urgent care centres from 16.5 to 19.1 million in the four years to 2007/08. But it called on PCTs to address gaps in the system due to lack of integration.

**Further information**
*Emergency care ten years on: reforming emergency care*, DH, April 2007.
*Not just a matter of time: a review of urgent and emergency care services in England*, Healthcare Commission, September 2008.

### NHS Direct

NHS Direct is a 24-hour telephone health advice and information service staffed by nurses. It provides callers to its helpline with information on what to do if they or their family are feeling ill, advice on particular health conditions, details of local healthcare services, such as doctors, dentists or late-night pharmacies, as well as self-help and support organisations. Staff use a computer-based decision-support system to suggest the best course of action, and can pass calls directly to emergency services; about 3 per cent of calls are emergencies.

Launched in 1998, NHS Direct employs almost 3,000 staff, of whom more than 1,200 are nurses. Its 36 call centres around the country handle 22,000 calls every day. NHS Direct's phone number provides a single point of access for out-of-hours care and handles all low-priority 999 ambulance calls. The top ten symptoms people call about are fever, abdominal pains, vomiting, rash, cough, diarrhoea, headache, cold or flu, toothache and chest pain. Typically, NHS Direct refers 11 per cent of callers to A&E, 28 per cent to their GP (10 per cent for urgent appointments), 5 per cent to walk-in centres, 4 per cent to a dentist and 3 per cent to a pharmacist. Nearly 70 per cent of calls are completed either by NHS Direct or with referral to routine in-hours services.

NHS Direct also offers services to other parts of the health service, including:
• out-of-hours support for GPs and dental services
• telephone support for patients with long-term conditions
• pre- and post-operative support for patients
• 24-hour response to health scares
• remote clinics via telephone.

PCTs acting in consortia commission most NHS Direct services. Formerly a special health authority, it became an NHS trust in April 2007.

NHS Direct in England and Wales operate from the same telephone number – 0845 4647 – while Scotland's information service is called NHS 24 and uses 08454 242424.
**www.nhsdirect.nhs.uk**

### NHS Direct Interactive
NHS Direct Interactive provides a health information service on two digital TV channels – via Teletext on Freeview, and on Sky. It does not broadcast programmes, but its 3,000 pages of content – available in 16 languages – on 500 topics include a health encyclopaedia, advice on diet, exercise, sexual health and smoking cessation, video clips on a range of health topics, a directory of local NHS services plus tips on using the NHS. Users can search for details of their nearest doctors, dentists, pharmacies and opticians by inputting their postcode details. Evidence suggests health information on digital TV can reach a wide audience, particularly people hard to reach through other means, such as those on low incomes or who may not have access to the internet.

### Ambulance services
Ambulance services have changed significantly in the past decade, with big improvements in response times for 999 calls, in training and quality of care, vehicle standards, equipment and technology. But as demand for ambulances is rising by an extra 250,000 responses a year, the Government has set a new strategic direction. The intention is to transform ambulance services to provide more diagnosis, treatment and care in people's homes, helping avoid unnecessary A&E admissions. In 2006, many of the 32 ambulance trusts merged to create 11 new organisations.

Ambulance services respond to 999 calls, doctors' urgent admission requests, high-dependency and inter-hospital transfers, referrals from NHS Direct and major incidents. In many areas ambulance trusts also provide transport to get patients to hospital for non-emergency treatment.

Key standards for ambulance services include responding to:
• 75 per cent of category A calls within eight minutes
• 95 per cent of category A calls within 19 minutes
• 95 per cent of category B calls within 19 minutes.

## Ambulance trust areas

Source: Department of Health

Since 2004, local NHS organisations have discretion over whether their ambulance service should automatically respond to category C calls: for these non-urgent conditions, callers may be referred to another NHS provider or treated at home.

NHS ambulances in England made 7.2 million urgent and emergency responses in 2007/08, of which 5.9 million calls resulted in an emergency response vehicle arriving on the scene.

The Ambulance Service Network (ASN) was established as part of the NHS Confederation to provide a strong and independent voice for UK ambulance services and to help them work more closely with the rest of the NHS. Launched in 2007, membership includes all ambulance trusts in England, those from the devolved administrations of Northern Ireland and Wales, as well as the islands of Guernsey, Jersey, Isle of Man and the Isle of Wight. Its work programme is steered by an independent board elected by its members.
www.nhsconfed.org/Networks/AmbulanceService

Crews now use satellite navigation systems, and emergency ambulances are equipped with technology such as ECG machines and telemetry, which lets crews send information about a patient's condition directly to the receiving hospital. As well as deploying solo responders such as motorcycles and rapid-response vehicles that can travel through heavy traffic more easily, ambulance trusts have introduced community responder schemes, which equip volunteers with a defibrillator and train them in basic life support. This is especially useful in remote areas.

Ambulance services are improving their ability to assess, diagnose and treat patients over the telephone and face to face. For example, new critical care paramedics – authorised to use pain-relief drugs and with enhanced resuscitation skills – are improving care for critically ill and injured patients. Emergency care practitioners assess, diagnose and treat minor illnesses and injuries in the community or in people's homes, helping reduce unnecessary A&E admissions. ECPs also support GPs in and out of hours by carrying out home visits. Ambulance staff are able to refer patients to other health and social care providers, including GPs, intermediate care services and falls teams. In parts of the country, ambulance services co-ordinate a single point of access to urgent care, ensuring patients get the most appropriate services for their clinical need.

**Further information**
*Taking healthcare to the patient: transforming NHS ambulance services*, DH, June 2005.
*A vision for emergency and urgent care: the role of ambulance services*, Ambulance Service Network/NHS Confederation, June 2008.

## Accident and emergency

Every year, about 11 million patients attend A&E departments in England, of whom 20 per cent are admitted to hospital as emergencies. Before a patient is admitted for further care, transferred or discharged, there can often be a lengthy chain of decisions, tests and treatment that can be subject to delay. Since 2004 A&E departments have had a target of seeing, diagnosing and treating all patients within four hours of their arrival. As a result, A&E departments have improved pre-admission and assessment procedures, as well as ensured better access to diagnostic facilities and equipment. Some have set up clinical decision units or have access to medical assessment units. Figures since 2005 show the NHS is generally meeting the four-hour target.

The DH's two national clinical directors for emergency care and for heart disease and stroke have argued for changes to how their services are delivered. They point out that traditional hospital A&E departments are no longer the only – or even the most – appropriate place to treat such conditions, despite recent improvements.

### Further information
*Emergency access – clinical case for change: report by Sir George Alberti, the national director for emergency access*, DH, December 2006.
*Mending hearts and brains – clinical case for change: report by Professor Roger Boyle, national director for heart disease and stroke*, DH, December 2006.

## Critical care

Critical care comprises intensive and high-dependence care services. A modernisation programme for critical care has integrated services for critically ill patients wherever they are in the health system. Key objectives were to:
• increase capacity
• develop services supporting critically ill patients throughout the hospital – not necessarily restricted to critical care 'units'
• provide an integrated critical care organisation within and between hospitals working in collaborative networks
• provide comprehensive information and data on critical care.

The number of adult critical care beds in January 2008 increased to 3,473 – the highest ever recorded in England and 3.4 per cent more than a year earlier. However, high levels of respiratory illness have increased demand for such beds.

**Further information**
*Comprehensive critical care – a review of adult critical care services*, DH, May 2000.

# Mental health

One sixth of the population suffers from a mental health problem every day. Mental illness accounts for a third of all illness and 40 per cent of all disability in Britain, while mental health services absorb 13.8 per cent of the NHS budget. Over five years, mental health spending increased by 30 per cent in real terms to £5.53 billion in 2007/08. New services and staff were introduced as a result of the mental health National Service Framework in 1999 and the NHS Plan in 2000. Since 1997 the number of consultant psychiatrists has risen by 1,300 (55 per cent), clinical psychologists by 2,700 (69 per cent) and mental health nurses by 10,000 (24 per cent).

Today, the principles guiding mental healthcare are:
- care provided closer to home
- earlier intervention
- 24/7 home treatment
- care tailored to individuals' needs
- better access to modern drugs
- care provided by multi-disciplinary teams
- more use of talking therapies.

## Organising mental health services

Mental health services are provided as part of primary and secondary care, with responsibility split between the NHS, social care and the independent and voluntary sectors. However, PCTs are responsible for commissioning all mental health services. There are about 50 specialist mental health trusts which provide acute inpatient care, community and rehabilitation services, residential care centres, day hospitals and drop-in centres. About 80,000 staff work in statutory mental health services.

## Primary and community services

Of people who receive help for mental health problems, 90 per cent are dealt with in primary care. In a typical PCT of 330,000 people, about 40,000 will suffer from depression, anxiety or other so-called mental disorders. Another 800 will have a psychotic illness such as schizophrenia. Of GP consultations, 30 per cent have a significant mental health component.

Nevertheless, 80 per cent of NHS spending on mental health is devoted to inpatient services. Less than half of GPs have postgraduate training in psychiatry and only 2 per cent of practice nurses have mental health training, although about half of GP surgeries provide counselling. The GMS contract (see page 198) gives GPs an incentive to provide care for the physical health of people with severe mental illness. GPs usually refer patients they cannot help directly to the local community mental health team (CMHT) or to a psychiatric outpatient clinic.

CMHTs – sometimes known as primary care liaison teams – are the main source of specialist support for those suffering severe and enduring mental health problems. They assess and monitor mental health needs using two specialist systems – the care programme approach or care management. These require that everyone seen by specialist mental health services should have their need for treatment assessed, a care plan drawn up and a named mental health worker to co-ordinate their care, including a regular review of their needs. They aim to help provide continuity of care across different services, promote multi-professional and inter-agency working, and ensure appropriate care for people diagnosed with serious mental illness on discharge from hospital.

CMHT members include community psychiatric nurses, social workers, psychologists, occupational therapists, doctors and support workers. Patients will regularly meet the psychiatrist from their mental health team at a psychiatric outpatient clinic for review of their treatment.

Providing mental health services in the community has prompted new approaches to care to avoid hospital admission. For example, by 2007 there were:
- 166 early intervention teams, which aim to treat psychotic illness as quickly and effectively as possible, especially during the critical period after its onset
- 251 assertive outreach teams to provide intensive support for severely mentally ill people who are difficult to engage in more traditional services
- 343 home treatment and crisis resolution teams to provide flexible acute care in patients' own homes with a 24-hour service to help with crises.

The Government is extending 'talking treatments' such as cognitive behaviour therapy for people with depression and anxiety disorders. The Improving Access to Psychological Therapies (IAPT) programme is encouraging provision outside hospital, in people's homes, GP practices, Job Centres and other community settings. After piloting in 13 PCTs, IAPT is gradually expanding, with £173 million investment over three years.

### Further information
*Briefing 157: Improving access to psychological therapies*, PCT Network/NHS Confederation, February 2008.
*Refocusing the care programme approach: policy and positive practice guidance*, DH, March 2008.

## Hospital services
Psychiatric hospital services have been progressively scaled down over the past 30 years, as many services are now provided in the community. England has 23 mental health beds per 100,000 population. However, numbers of patients detained under the Mental Health Act have been rising, intensifying pressure on beds and stress on staff. One result has been a significant increase in pressure on hospital services, with psychiatric beds experiencing high occupancy rates – more than one-third of wards exceed capacity. Acute inpatient services deal mainly with patients suffering severe mental illness.

## Child and adolescent mental health services
One in ten children has a clinically significant mental health problem. Child and adolescent mental health services (CAMHS) cater for young people and children with all types of mental disorder, including hyperkinetic disorders. Services are arranged into four tiers, which should be closely linked:
- tier 1 includes services contributing to mental healthcare of children and young people, but whose primary function is not mental healthcare (for example, schools and GPs)
- tier 2 includes mental health professionals assessing and treating those who do not respond at tier 1
- tier 3 includes teams of mental health professionals providing multi-disciplinary interventions for more complex problems
- tier 4 includes the most severe and complex problems that cannot be dealt with at tier 3, including inpatient and specialist services such as eating disorders.

Mental health trusts are the principal providers of CAMHS, although PCTs, local authorities and the independent sector also provide services. Since 2006 all areas have been required to have 'comprehensive CAMHS', including out-of-hours emergency cover as well as adequate provision for all young people up to age 18 with mental health problems. However, many are still far from meeting this requirement.

A national review of CAMHS during 2008 called for changes over the next five years to include:
- children's mental health and psychological well-being services to be viewed as a single service
- in all services, staff trained to promote mental health and psychological well-being, intervene early and be aware of how to call on more specialised services
- easy-to-access, readily available and evidence-based specialist services.

The Government has set up a National Advisory Council on Children's Mental Health and Psychological Wellbeing to ensure the recommendations are carried out.

**Further information**
*Children and young people in mind: the final report of the national CAMHS review*, DCSF/DH, November 2008.

## Forensic services
Forensic mental health services deal with mentally ill people who may need a degree of physical security and have shown challenging behaviour beyond the scope of general psychiatric services. Some may be mentally disordered offenders.

Services fall into three categories:
- low-security services tend to be based near general psychiatric wards in NHS hospitals
- medium-secure services often operate regionally and usually consist of locked wards with a greater number and a wider range of staff
- high-security services are provided by the three special hospitals (Ashworth, Broadmoor and Rampton), which have much greater levels of security and care for people who pose an immediate and serious risk to others.

In addition, new services are developing to meet the needs of mentally disordered offenders in the community.

## Modernising services

The National Service Framework for mental health, published in 1999, set out a ten-year programme to introduce new standards of care that people could expect in every part of the country. It emphasised mental health promotion, primary care and access, effective services for people with severe mental illness, caring about carers and reducing suicide by at least one fifth by 2010.

Eight years after the NSF was published, the national director for mental health noted that focus had shifted from specialist mental health services to whole-community mental health. Policy emphasis is now on breaking down traditional boundaries – between professional groups, between primary and secondary care, between the NHS and the independent sector and between health services and other agencies such as education and employment. Current priorities are:

- social inclusion – linking better care to opportunities for employment and training
- psychological therapies – especially extending availability of cognitive therapy
- services for ethnic minorities – removing inequalities in patient experience
- new powers under the Mental Health Act 2007 – to treat high-risk patients in the community who would otherwise go untreated.

The DH has set out a national framework within which patients will have more choice over mental health services. It promises service users the power to choose their own path through services as well as to exercise their preferences over how, when, where and what treatments they receive.

### Further information

*National service framework for mental health: modern standards and service models*, DH, September 1999.
*Mental health ten years on: progress on mental health care reform*, DH, April 2007.
*Breaking down barriers – clinical case for change: report by Louis Appleby, national director for mental health*, DH, May 2007.
*A new vision for mental health: discussion paper*, The Future Vision Coalition, July 2008.
Choices in Mental Health website **www.mhchoice.csip.org.uk**

The Mental Health Network was established as part of the NHS Confederation to provide a distinct and independent voice for mental health and learning disability service providers. Launched in 2007, membership includes mental health trusts, independent sector members and PCTs that deliver NHS mental health services. The network aims to improve the system for patients and staff by raising the profile of mental health issues and increasing the influence of mental health and disability providers. Its work programme is steered by an independent board elected by its members.
www.nhsconfed.org/Networks/MentalHealth

### Delivering race equality in mental healthcare

One in five mental health inpatients comes from a black and minority ethnic (BME) background, compared to about one in ten of the population as a whole. This initiative was launched in 2005 and outlines a five-year action plan for achieving equality and tackling discrimination in mental health services in England and for all people of black and minority ethnic status. Delivering race equality (DRE) is part of a wider programme of action to develop greater equality in health and social care.

The programme is based on three building blocks:

- providing more appropriate and responsive services and improving clinical services for groups such as older people, asylum seekers, refugees and children
- engaging communities in planning services, supported by 500 new community development workers; more than 350 were in post by 2008
- improving ethnicity monitoring, dissemination of information and knowledge about effective service, including a regular census of mental health patients.

The intention is that by 2010 mental health services will be characterised by 'less fear' among BME communities and service users; increased satisfaction with services; a reduced rate of admission of people from BME communities to psychiatric inpatient units; a reduction in the disproportionate rates of compulsory detention of BME service users in inpatient units and a more balanced range of culturally appropriate and effective therapies.

Eighteen focused implementation sites have been established across the country to help identify and spread best practice. The evaluation of these sites is informing national implementation. A BME mental health programme board, directly accountable to ministers, is overseeing this action plan and the wider BME mental health programme.

**Further information**
*Delivering race equality in mental health care: progress review of focused implementation sites – national summary*, National DRE Programme, January 2007.
*Briefing 158: Delivering race equality in mental health care*, MHN/NHS Confederation, March 2008.
Delivering Race Equality **www.actiondre.org.uk**

**Revising mental health law: the Mental Health Act 2007**
The Mental Health Act 2007 updates the Mental Health Act 1983 through seven major amendments, while an eighth amendment updates the Mental Capacity Act 2005. These provide better safeguards for service users, with new rights to advocacy, a say in who their nearest relative is and the right to refuse electro-convulsive therapy and other treatments.

The amendments include:
• a simplified definition of mental disorder
• a wider definition of medical treatment
• the introduction of supervised community treatment after initial detention and treatment in hospital
• additional safeguards for service users
• changes to professional roles to allow a wider range to adopt the functions traditionally delivered by approved social workers and medical professionals
• improved access to review tribunals
• abolition of finite restriction orders.

**Further information**
*Briefing 171: Implementing the Mental Health Act 2007: what boards need to know*, MHN/NHS Confederation, September 2008.

# Care for special groups

## Prison healthcare

People in prison have generally poorer health than the population at large: 90 per cent have a mental health or substance misuse problem or both, and 80 per cent smoke. Since 2006, PCTs have been responsible for commissioning healthcare for prisons. The aim is to provide prisoners with access to the same quality and range of healthcare services as the public receives from the NHS. Schemes to tackle smoking and drug misuse and vaccinate against hepatitis B have since begun. Prisons have also implemented a new care-planning system for prisoners at risk of suicide.

A national partnership agreement between the DH and the Home Office on behalf of the Prison Service underpins the local partnership arrangements between PCTs and public sector prisons.

In a joint initiative, the DH, Department for Children, Schools and Families, Ministry of Justice, Youth Justice Board and the Home Office consulted on how health and social care services can be improved for people subject to the criminal justice system. The Government is now developing a national offender health and social care strategy, to be published during 2009.

### Further information

*National partnership agreement between the Department of Health and the Home Office for the accountability and commissioning of health services for prisoners in public sector prisons in England*, DH, January 2007.
*Good practice in prison health*, DH, July 2007.
*Independent evaluation report of Improving health, supporting justice: a consultation document*, DH, August 2008.
*Commissioning healthcare in prisons*, Healthcare Commission/HM Inspectorate of Prisons, February 2009.
*Actions speak louder: a second review of healthcare in the community for young people who offend*, Healthcare Commission/HM Inspectorate of Probation, February 2009.
Prison Health Development Network **www.hsmc.bham.ac.uk/prisonhealth**

## Defence Medical Services

The Defence Medical Services comprise the Surgeon Generals Department, Joint Medical Command and the primary care services of the army, Royal Navy and Royal Air Force. DMS is headed by the Surgeon General and the Deputy Chief of Defence Staff (Health), and over 7,000 regular uniformed medical personnel from all three services belong to it.

DMS runs six Ministry of Defence hospital units based in the NHS, 15 rehabilitation units across the UK and Germany and 15 departments of community mental health. It also provides primary care to serving personnel and some dependants in the UK and to all 258,000 serving personnel and entitled dependants abroad – mainly in Germany, Cyprus and Gibraltar. It interacts with the NHS at many levels: for example, its healthcare professionals train in the NHS, while 1,600 NHS staff belong to the British Reserve Forces. A partnership of seven NHS trusts provides inpatient mental healthcare to serving personnel across the UK under contract to the Ministry of Defence.

Since 2008 all military veterans have been entitled to priority access to NHS secondary care for any conditions likely to be related to their service. There are about 5 million veterans in England. They are most likely to make use of audiology, mental health and orthopaedic services.

The NHS and MoD have launched six community mental health pilot sites (including one in Scotland) designed to make available within the NHS expert assessment and treatment for veterans with mental health problems.

### Further information
*Seventh report of session 2007/08: medical care for the armed forces*, House of Commons defence committee, February 2008.
*Meeting the healthcare needs of armed forces personnel, their families and veterans*, DH, December 2008.
*A review of the clinical governance of the Defence Medical Services in the UK and overseas*, Healthcare Commission, March 2009.
*The Nation's Commitment: Cross-Government Support to our Armed Forces, their Families and Veterans*, MoD, July 2008.
www.mod.uk/DefenceInternet/microsite/dms

### Healthcare for asylum seekers and refugees
People with an outstanding application for refuge in the UK are entitled to use NHS services without charge; the High Court ruled in 2008 that failed asylum seekers may still be deemed 'ordinarily resident' in the UK and so also entitled to free NHS treatment.

Asylum seekers are often from very different cultures, may not understand the principles behind the NHS, may not speak English and may have complex healthcare requirements.

The DH's Asylum Seeker Co-ordination Team (ASCT) co-ordinates healthcare policy for asylum seekers and refugees. ASCT works across the DH and other government departments, and with health workers and service planners in the field. In particular, it liaises with the Home Office to try to ensure that health and social care needs are met at all stages of the asylum process and taken into account in policy planning.

Asylum seekers usually stay in a network of induction centres on their arrival. Here they undergo an initial health assessment, normally by a nurse with access to a GP. Each asylum seeker is issued with a national hand-held health record.

The best model of healthcare for asylum seekers is integration into existing mainstream services. Where this is not possible immediately, the NHS locally may have to consider dedicated initiatives appropriate for asylum seekers new to an area. Some PCTs ensure there is space on GMS surgery lists for asylum seekers; others use personal medical services to set up surgeries for local vulnerable populations, which may include asylum seekers. PCTs and local councils are responsible for ensuring adequate access to interpreters for asylum seekers within their own area.

**Further information**
*Caring for dispersed asylum seekers: a resource pack*, DH, June 2003.
*Unheard voices – listening to the views of asylum-seekers and refugees*, Commission for Patient and Public Involvement in Health, May 2006.

# 04 Policy and strategy: creating a 'vision' for the NHS

**Making and implementing policy is a key strand of the Department of Health's work, and since the present Government came to power in 1997 it has published a plethora of major policy documents designed to improve health and social care, turning political vision into action.**

The Government regards its NHS reform programme as having progressed through three phases:
- beginning with the NHS Plan in 2000, capacity and investment were increased across the service
- levers to enable reform were introduced, such as choice, contestability, more freedom for providers and new financial systems
- following the Next Stage Review (see opposite) the NHS must concentrate on using the extra capacity and reform levers to achieve high-quality care and value for money.

Policy and strategy are aimed at the long term (such as the Next Stage Review's ten-year timeframe), the medium term (such as the three-year cycle of the NHS's operational plans) and the short-term (such as the annual operating framework). And apart from initiatives specific to the health and social care system, the NHS is influenced by cross-government policy and strategy frameworks such as the comprehensive spending review and public service agreements.

NHS system reforms have improved management of the health service but need more time to deliver significant benefits for patients. A study by the Audit Commission and Healthcare Commission found some reforms beginning to work, with better financial management and a more business-like approach encouraged by payment by results and foundation trusts. Evidence suggested competition from independent organisations had improved services in places and standards were improving.

But other changes needed more time to deliver significant results, with limited progress on moving care out of hospitals and closer to home. The commissions advised further nationally imposed structural changes should be avoided as progress had been hampered by two major reorganisations since the reforms were introduced. Under-developed commissioning and weak monitoring had also hindered progress.

**Further information**
*Is the treatment working? Progress with the NHS system reform programme,*
Audit Commission and Healthcare Commission, June 2008.

# Next Stage Review

## Background and principles

After ten years of far-reaching and fundamental reform, the Government announced its NHS Next Stage Review in 2007, intended to establish strategy for the next ten years. Headed by health minister and surgeon Lord Darzi, the review aimed to 'build on the progress made in delivering the vision set out in the NHS Plan and the Government's reform agenda', while identifying 'the way forward for a 21st-century NHS which is clinically driven, patient-centred and responsive to local communities'. Conducted over 12 months, it involved 60,000 patients, public and staff, including 2,000 clinicians. Lord Darzi declared the changes it proposed would be clinically led and driven by local staff rather than 'top-down' targets.

The review's interim report, *Our NHS, our future*, described a vision of a 'world-class' NHS that is:
- fair – equally available to all, taking full account of personal circumstances and diversity
- personalised – tailored to individuals' needs and wants, especially those of the most vulnerable and those in greatest need, providing access to services at the time and place of their choice
- effective – focused on delivering outcomes for patients that are among the best in the world
- safe – giving patients and the public confidence in the care they receive
- locally accountable – so that staff are empowered to lead change and innovate locally, based on clinical evidence, meeting local needs and after engaging with patients and the public.

The subsequent report, *Leading local change*, further pledged:
- change will always be to patients' benefit – improving clinical outcomes, experience or safety
- change will be clinically driven – led by clinicians and based on best available evidence
- all change will be locally led – being a universal service is not the same as being uniform, and local needs are best met by local solutions
- you will be involved – patients, carers, the public and other key partners, with those affected able to have their say while NHS organisations work openly and collaboratively
- you will see the difference first – existing services will not be withdrawn until new and better services are available.

## Recommendations for change

The Next Stage Review aims to create an NHS 'that gives patients more information and choice, works in partnership and has quality of care at its heart'. Among its recommendations are:

- an NHS Constitution (see opposite)
- patients to have a right to all NICE-approved drugs
- patients to have a legal right to choice of any provider, including GP
- all PCTs to commission well-being and prevention services
- payments to hospitals to depend on quality of care as well as volume
- no additional top-down targets beyond the minimum standards
- every provider of NHS services to measure, analyse and improve quality, displaying it to staff through 'clinical dashboards'
- clinical leadership to be strengthened
- an NHS Leadership Council (see page 20).

The review made additional recommendations for primary care (see page 71), while the ten strategic health authorities set out local improvements in eight care pathways, the main themes of which were:

- more support and advice to stay healthy
- greater choice and a more personal experience for women in childbirth
- children's services to be better designed around children's and families' needs
- specialised centres for major trauma, heart attack and stroke care
- more care closer to people's homes
- extending mental health services in the community, notably for psychological therapies
- personalised partnerships between people and professionals for long-term conditions
- greater dignity and respect at the end of life.

The review avoided further organisational restructuring and creating new bodies. But uncertainty remains about how some of the broad statements of direction will be translated into detailed policy and how implementation will be managed. The review's emphasis on local leadership in preference to top-down instruction represents a major culture shift and may pose the biggest challenge: significant central control still exists. In the longer term, impatience with the pace of change may result in renewed central instruction.

**Key text: NHS Constitution**

'The NHS belongs to the people...' A draft constitution intended to enshrine the NHS's principles and values for the future was developed as part of the Next Stage Review. It applies only to the NHS in England and comprises:

- seven key principles that govern how the NHS operates, such as providing a comprehensive service and value for money
- 37 rights and pledges to patients and the public about matters such as access, quality, respect, choice and complaints
- nine responsibilities that patients and public owe the NHS, such as keeping appointments and treating staff with respect
- ten staff rights concerning issues such as working environment, fair pay, representation and equal treatment
- 11 staff responsibilities, including patient confidentiality and professional accountability
- six values, including respect and dignity, commitment to quality and compassion.

The Constitution attempts a balance between the need for clarity and avoiding litigation, between enshrining enduring values and principles while ensuring the NHS has flexibility to change. The Health Bill 2009 will place a duty on all NHS organisations, private and third sector providers in England to take account of the Constitution. The Government will be obliged by law to renew the Constitution every ten years, so that changes cannot take place without debate.

**Further information**

*Briefing 167: The NHS Constitution*, NHS Confederation, July 2008.
*The National Health Service Constitution: report of the constitutional advisory forum to the Secretary of State for Health*, DH, December 2008.
*The NHS Constitution for England*, NHS, January 2009.
*The handbook to the NHS Constitution for England*, DH, January 2009.
*The statement of NHS accountability for England*, DH, January 2009.

The House of Commons health committee felt many of the Next Stage Review's recommendations had been made in previous white papers, and that the review differed from its predecessors mainly in its extensive consultation with clinicians and patients. The committee doubted that PCTs were capable of implementing the recommendations, criticising the review for not ranking priorities and being imprecise about costs.

**Further information**

*Our NHS, our future: NHS Next Stage Review – interim report*, DH, October 2007.
*NHS Next Stage Review: leading local change*, DH, May 2008.
*High quality care for all: NHS Next Stage Review final report*, DH, June 2008.
*NHS Next Stage Review: our vision for primary and community care*, DH, July 2008.
*Engagement analysis: NHS Next Stage Review – what we heard from the Our NHS, our future process*, DH, July 2008.
*Briefing 168: High-quality care for all*, NHS Confederation, July 2008.
*Briefing 169: NHS Next Stage Review: a vision for primary and community care*, PCTN/NHS Confederation, July 2008.
*First report of session 2008–09: NHS Next Stage Review*, House of Commons health committee, January 2009.
www.ournhs.nhs.uk

## The planning framework

The Government sets long-term strategy for public services every few years during a comprehensive spending review. It also decides the financial settlement for every government department and publishes public service agreements that contain its priority outcomes for the CSR period. In turn, the Department of Health publishes its priorities in its business plan, while the NHS operating framework outlines priorities for the health service over a three-year planning cycle.

### Comprehensive spending review (CSR)

The CSR is a long-term and fundamental review of all Government expenditure. The first was held in 1998 and the second in 2007.

The 2007 CSR contended that far-reaching social, economic and technological changes – as well as shifts in public expectations and attitudes – have transformed the environment in which public services operate. It stated that 'public services need to be ready to respond to these trends', and said the new model of public service delivery should be based on excellent outcomes, personalisation and value for money. It defined personalised services as those that are flexible and tailored to individuals' needs, that treat people with care, respect their preferences and appreciate the value of their time.

The 2007 CSR also set the NHS's financial allocation for the subsequent three years:
- spending will increase by 4 per cent a year in real terms, compared to 7.4 per cent between 2002 and 2007
- funding is available for Next Stage initiatives, including a strategy to reduce health inequalities, new services for people with long-term conditions, measures to increase GP access, schemes to cut waiting times for cancer services, introducing named midwives for all pregnant women, MRSA screening and other measures to combat healthcare-associated infections
- £500 million of capital from the sale of surplus property will be reinvested in the NHS
- the NHS is expected to make 3 per cent a year in efficiency savings.

However, the 'global economic downturn' has since had a major impact on the financial climate, and the Government's 2008 pre-Budget report made clear that the NHS – along with other public services – would have to play a part in supporting the economy 'through these difficult times' (see page 181).

### Further information
*The 2007 comprehensive spending review and pre-Budget report*, HM Treasury, October 2007.
*Briefing 151: 2007 comprehensive spending review*, NHS Confederation, October 2007.

## Public service agreements (PSAs)
Before 2007, each government department drew up a public service agreement with the Treasury, setting out what it was expected to provide with its resources over a three-year period. After the last CSR, the Government published a set of 30 PSAs cutting across departments. Each PSA is underpinned by a single delivery agreement shared across all contributing departments, which sets out plans for achieving the PSA targets and the role of key partners. The DH is leading two PSAs:
- PSA 18 – promoting better health and well-being for all
- PSA 19 – ensuring better care for all.

At the end of 2008 the DH reported 'some progress' on PSA 18, with two of the five measures against which it is judged showing improvement; progress on PSA 19 was 'strong', with six out of eight measures improving.

## The new NHS – modern, dependable
The Labour Government's first health white paper after coming to power, published in December 1997. It announced the setting up of primary care groups (forerunners of PCTs), NICE, the Commission for Health Improvement (forerunner of the Care Quality Commission) and NHS Direct, describing reforms that would be 'a new model for a new century'.

## The NHS Plan
The NHS Plan is the foundation of the Government's reforms for modernising the health service, and links change explicitly to extra investment announced in the March 2000 Budget. Published in July 2000 and intended as an ambitious ten-year programme, the Plan set out to tackle 'systematic problems, which date from 1948 when the NHS was formed'.

## Shifting the balance of power within the NHS
Two documents – *Securing delivery* (July 2001) and *The next steps* (January 2002) – outlined the rationale behind devolving power from Whitehall to frontline NHS organisations, in particular PCTs. They announced that SHAs were to replace the existing 95 health authorities and that the DH would have a reduced role in directly managing the NHS.

## Delivering the NHS Plan: next steps on investment, next steps on reform
This document, published in April 2002, introduced plans to reform the NHS's financial flows through payment by results, brought new emphasis to patient choice and underlined commitment to promoting diversity in supply of healthcare through joint ventures with the private sector.

## The NHS Improvement Plan: putting people at the heart of public services
Published in June 2004, this 'supports the ongoing commitment to a ten-year process of reform first set out in the NHS Plan' but adds some new priorities to be achieved by 2008: giving patients more information and extending patient choice through 'personalised care', improving support for people with long-term conditions and stronger emphasis on disease prevention.

## Creating a patient-led NHS: delivering the NHS Improvement Plan
In this document, published in March 2005, the Government revealed it wanted 'some radically different types of provision' that would 'involve freeing up the entrepreneurialism within primary care and developing new types of provider organisations'.

### Our health, our care, our say
Published in January 2006, this white paper set out the Government's vision for more effective health and social care services outside hospital, calling for closer integration between health and social services, better access to GPs, improved care for people with long-term conditions and further effort to combat health inequalities.

### Health reform in England: update and commissioning framework
In July 2006, six years after the NHS Plan, this document reported progress and set out commissioning arrangements for hospital services covered by choice and payment by results.

### Our NHS, our future: NHS Next Stage Review – interim report
Issued to coincide with the comprehensive spending review in October 2007, this stressed that the NHS should complete current reforms, not do something different. It called for improved access to GPs and screening of all admissions for MRSA. It described a vision of the NHS as fair, personalised, effective and safe.

### High quality care for all: NHS Next Stage Review – final report
Coinciding with the NHS's 60th anniversary in July 2008, this report and a suite of others accompanying it sought to plot a direction for the next ten years (see page 113).

Ten other PSAs are relevant to the NHS:
- improving the health and well-being of children and young people
- improving children and young people's safety
- addressing the disadvantage individuals experience because of their gender, race, disability, age, sexual orientation, religion or belief
- increasing the proportion of socially excluded adults in settled accommodation and employment, education or training
- tackling poverty and promoting greater independence and well-being in later life
- reducing the harm caused by alcohol and drugs
- leading the global effort to avoid dangerous climate change
- securing a healthy natural environment for today and the future
- reducing poverty in poorer countries through quicker progress towards the millennium development goals.

The Government says the new-style PSAs mark a move from top-down targets to more local flexibility.

The DH's own priorities for 2008/09 included:
• preparing for a flu pandemic
• developing the strategy for reforming social care
• leading local transformation of the NHS
• reducing inequalities
• reducing the burden of lifestyle diseases
• helping improve value for money.

**Further information**
*Department of Health business plan 2008–09*, DH, April 2008.
*Department of Health autumn performance report 2008*, TSO, December 2008.

## NHS priorities 2008–11

The NHS's programme is set out in the operating framework for 2009/10, the second year of the three-year planning cycle. As with PSAs, the Government is keen to give NHS organisations more local flexibility over their priorities. The operating framework therefore combines a small number of compulsory national priorities with areas where PCTs can decide themselves how they meet the target. They also have the chance to add their own priorities.

The compulsory national priorities were established in last year's operating framework and remain:
• improving cleanliness and tackling healthcare-associated infections
• achieving the maximum 18-week referral to treatment waiting time and improving access to GPs
• improving the health of adults and children, and reducing health inequalities
• improving patient experience, staff satisfaction and engagement
• preparing to respond to an emergency such as a flu pandemic.

Progress so far includes:
• halving MRSA infections since 2003/04 and reducing *C. difficile* infections by 35 per cent on the previous year
• meeting the 18-week target nationally five months early
• achieving more than half of GP practices offering extended opening hours, three months ahead of target.

In developing their own local priorities after consultation with their communities and partners, PCTs are expected to be influenced in 2009/10 by the Next Stage Review, especially concerning:

- alcohol
- dementia
- end-of-life care
- mental health
- military personnel, their dependants and veterans
- mixed-sex accommodation
- people living in vulnerable circumstances
- people with learning disabilities.

**Further information**
*Operational plans 2008/09–2010/11: national planning guidance and 'vital signs'*, DH, January 2008.
*The operating framework for the NHS in England 2009/10*, DH, December 2008.
*Briefing 172: The operating framework for the NHS in England 2009/10*, NHS Confederation, December 2008.

## Equality and diversity
Eliminating discrimination and disadvantage in the healthcare workforce and reducing health inequalities in the population are major policy aims of the DH and the NHS.

To that end, the DH devised a 'single equality scheme' (SES) for 2007–10, detailing how it plans to meet its obligations under equality legislation. The SES states: 'The Department has a central role in leading the field in relation to equality and human rights, and the key to making a positive difference to the quality of people's lives starts with policy making that has equality and human rights at its core.'

The scheme covers the DH's responsibility for the health and social care system and as an employer in its own right. It is based on six strands:

- race
- gender
- disability
- age
- sexual orientation
- religion and belief.

These reflect the fact that inequality and prejudice are often perceived and experienced on many levels. By law the DH must undertake equality impact assessments relating to race, disability and gender to ensure its policies do not inadvertently disadvantage any groups, but DH assessments under the SES also include age, sexual orientation and religion and belief. Action plans detail specific areas in which the DH pursues equality and human rights.

Within the DH, the equality and human rights group (EHRG) aims to:
- give strategic leadership on equality and human rights
- champion equality and human rights within the DH
- challenge discrimination across the DH, NHS and social care
- advise on proposed legislation
- devise innovative change programmes
- develop partnerships with stakeholders, regulators, patients and staff.

The Pacesetters programme is a partnership between the DH, NHS and local communities experiencing health inequalities. It aims both to reduce health inequalities and produce working environments that are fair and free of discrimination. Six strategic health authorities and three trusts within each SHA area are working with the EHRG on issues that include promoting dignity and respect, tackling bullying and improving the health status of Gypsies and Travellers.

Individual NHS trusts are also encouraged to develop their own single equality schemes, bringing together their responses to all six strands of the SES.

**Further information**
*Single equality scheme*, DH, June 2007.
*A dialogue of equals: the Pacesetters programme community engagement guide*, DH, January 2008.
*Navigating equality and diversity: guidance for the NHS*, NHS Employers, April 2008.
*Making the difference: the Pacesetters beginner's guide to service improvement for equality and diversity in the NHS*, DH, July 2008.
*Briefing 48: Single equality schemes in the NHS: the developing picture*, NHS Employers, November 2008.
**www.nhsemployers.org/equality**

# 05 Quality and safety

The NHS is committed to providing high-quality care, which means continually striving to improve clinical standards, using resources efficiently and ensuring patients' safety. Quality and safety criteria are set and monitored nationally, with every organisation's performance assessed and made public. Recent concerns about healthcare-acquired infections have brought renewed emphasis on patient safety.

## Ensuring quality

The Government's first health policy white paper, *The new NHS: modern, dependable*, published in 1997, promised that the service 'will have quality at its heart'. Its most recent, the Next Stage Review's *High quality care for all*, says: 'Enabling all parts of the NHS to focus consistently and systematically on improving the quality of care is a major challenge. It requires a long-term transformation that touches all parts of the system, starting from the front line.' The aim is to move from high-quality care in some aspects of what the NHS does to high-quality care in all. The review insisted that quality be understood from the patient's perspective, and defined it as comprising:
• patient safety
• patient experience
• effectiveness of care.

NHS organisations have a statutory duty to ensure the quality of their services, just as they have always had to keep their organisations financially solvent. Indeed, they will by law have to publish 'quality accounts' from 2010. These will be reports on the quality of their services, examining safety, experience and outcomes.

Trust chief executives are accountable for clinical standards, and each trust has a designated senior clinician who must make sure clinical governance systems are functioning properly. Primary care trusts have to nominate a senior health professional, usually a GP, to lead on clinical standards and professional development. As commissioners, PCTs are now also to be held to account for the quality of health outcomes they achieve for their populations, including the most vulnerable or excluded people with complex needs. Each strategic health authority is setting up a 'quality observatory' to enable services to be benchmarked, develop ways of measuring quality and help staff improve services.

An initiative of the Next Stage Review, the NQB is intended to provide strategic oversight and leadership in quality across the service and is chaired by the NHS chief executive. Other members include the NHS medical director, chief medical and nursing officers and the chairs of the Care Quality Commission, NICE and Monitor. It also has four expert and four lay representatives.

The board's role is to 'align quality at all levels in the NHS', from clinical teams to SHAs. It will oversee work to improve quality indicators, advise the Secretary of State on priorities for clinical standards set by NICE and report annually on the state of quality using internationally agreed measures.

## Clinical governance

Clinical governance is an explicit framework for making all NHS staff accountable for quality improvement and safeguarding standards. The chief medical officer's definition of clinical governance is:

> a system through which NHS organisations are accountable for continuously improving the quality of their services and safeguarding high standards of care, by creating an environment in which clinical excellence will flourish.

It seeks to transform the culture, ways of working and systems of every health organisation so that patient safety, quality assurance and improvement are an integral part of their everyday work. Its main features are a coherent approach to quality improvement, clear lines of accountability for clinical quality systems and effective processes for identifying and managing risk and addressing poor performance.

Its essential components are:
- the patient's experience – of access to services, organisation of care, humanity of care and the care environment
- the organisation's use of information
- consultation and patient involvement
- risk management
- clinical audit
- effectiveness and research
- staffing and staff management
- education, training and continuing professional development

- leadership
- direction and planning, accountability and structures
- partnership with the public
- partnership with the local health economy.

For clinical governance to work properly and quality to flourish, NHS organisations must foster a culture of openness and participation, value education and research, and encourage people to learn from failures. Good practice and new approaches should be shared readily and received willingly.

**Key text:** *A first class service: quality in the new NHS*
Published in June 1998, this provides the blueprint for ensuring quality. Its main themes are the importance of national consistency in implementing evidence-based practice, accountability for local best practice, commitment to a coherent system of quality improvement and assurance, provision for managing poor performance and professional collaboration and teamwork.

The Essence of Care guidelines reinforce the measures to improve quality in *A first class service*, enabling NHS organisations to benchmark the fundamentals of good-quality care. In 2007 the DH published the eleventh in the series, which covered the care environment. It proposed best practice in this area should mean the environment:
- is easily and safely accessible
- is tidy and well-maintained
- is consistently clean
- makes patients and visitors feel confident that infection control precautions are in place
- makes patients feel comfortable, safe, reassured, confident and welcome
- meets patients' individual needs
- makes patients and carers feel confident the team is well led and all members are competent
- has adequate and well-maintained supplies when required for the patient.

**Further information**
*Essence of care: patient-focused benchmarks for clinical governance*, DH, April 2003.
*Improving quality and safety – progress in implementing clinical governance in primary care: lessons for the new primary care trusts*, National Audit Office, January 2007.
*Essence of care: environment benchmark*, DH, August 2007.

## Clinical audit

Clinical audit is an important instrument of clinical governance, providing rich data to support service improvement, better information for patients and revalidation of clinicians. In 2006 the chief medical officer called for clinical audit to be reinvigorated, and a National Clinical Audit Advisory Group has now been set up. The group is establishing a 'wide and inclusive' forum to decide priorities. NCAAG also acts as the steering group for the national clinical audit and patients' outcomes programme, which commissions national audits, consults those with an interest in clinical audit and develops resources for them.

In 2008, for the first time, the NHS in England released survival rates for four common cardiac and orthopaedic operations for each trust, published on the NHS Choices website. The figures revealed all hospitals were performing acceptably and five were above average. Data for a wider range of elective and emergency surgery will be made available in due course.

### Further information

*Good doctors, safer patients: proposals to strengthen the system to assure and improve the performance of doctors and to protect the safety of patients*, DH, July 2006.
*Trust, assurance and safety – the regulation of health professionals in the 21st century*, TSO, February 2007.

Key organisation: **Health Care Standards Unit**
Based at Keele University, HCSU was set up in 2004 to support and develop the use of standards in the DH and NHS. It maintains detailed information banks on quality standards, comprising policy documents, related research, management tools and central guidance. It also carries out research on the usability and impact of standards.
**www.hcsu.org.uk**

### Developing integrated governance

NHS boards' decisions must take note not only of clinical governance but of corporate governance, research governance, information governance and financial governance. As the NHS engages with a wider range of partners than ever before, governance between organisations has become crucial too. These strands of governance have developed independently from each other, and do not necessarily align or inter-relate: for example, financial allocations may not always take fully into account the pressures of clinical governance. But in reality, these domains all complement and impact on one another. Creating different structures to manage and monitor them can lead to duplication and wasted effort, overburdening staff with demands for data.

Some NHS organisations have begun to streamline their governance activities. However, integrating the strands of governance is not easy, and much detail remains to be worked out.

**Further information**
*Integrated governance handbook*, DH, February 2006.

## National service frameworks
National service frameworks (NSFs) are evidence-based programmes setting quality standards and specifying services that should be available for a particular condition or care group across the whole NHS. They are intended to eradicate local variations in standards and services, raise standards generally, promote collaboration between organisations and contribute to improving public health. Each identifies key interventions, puts in place a strategy to support implementation and establishes an agreed timescale.

Each NSF is developed with assistance from an external reference group of health professionals, service users and carers, health service managers, partner agencies and other advocates. The DH supports the groups and manages the overall process.

Usually only one new NSF is released in a year. The programme so far covers:
• paediatric intensive care: January 1997
• mental health, September 1999
• coronary heart disease, March 2000
• cancer, September 2000; cancer reform strategy, December 2007
• older people, March 2001
• diabetes: standards, December 2001; delivery strategy, January 2003
• renal services: part one, January 2004; part two, February 2005
• children, young people and maternity services, September 2004
• long-term conditions, March 2005
• chronic obstructive pulmonary disease, pending.

## Quality and Outcomes Framework

The QOF is a means of encouraging high-quality services in general practice, and was introduced as part of the new general medical services contract in 2004. It sets out a range of national standards based on the best available research evidence. The standards are divided into four domains:

- clinical standards linked to the care of patients suffering from chronic disease
- organisational standards relating to records and information, communicating with patients, education and training, medicines management and clinical and practice management
- additional services, covering cervical screening, child health surveillance, maternity services and contraceptive services
- patient experience, including assessing access to GP appointments measured by the GP patient survey.

A set of indicators has been developed for each domain to describe different aspects of performance. Practices are free to choose the domains they want to focus on and the quality standards to which they aspire.

## Patient surveys

Listening to patients' views is essential for a patient-centred health service. To deliver improvements, the NHS has to know what people need and expect from it, and how well they think the service has responded to their needs and expectations. The programme of national patient surveys has three aims:

- to provide feedback for local quality improvement
- to assess users' experience for performance ratings, inspections and reviews
- to monitor patients' experience nationally.

Since 2002, several million patients have taken part in surveys. The Care Quality Commission (see page 158) is now responsible for carrying out national survey programmes. Trusts can seek support in carrying out their surveys from the NHS Surveys advice centre.

Surveys have included adult inpatients in acute hospitals, primary care trusts and community mental health services. In 2007, a total of 76,000 adult patients from 165 acute and specialist NHS trusts took part, and 92 per cent rated their care favourably.

The Dignity in Care campaign aims to raise care standards and encourage people to become 'dignity champions', spreading best practice and giving advice to other health and social care workers. High-quality services that respect people's dignity should:

- have zero tolerance of all forms of abuse
- treat people as individuals by offering a personalised service
- enable people to exercise maximum independence, choice and control
- listen and support people to express their needs and wants
- respect people's right to privacy
- ensure people feel able to complain without fear of retribution
- engage with family members and carers as care partners
- assist people to maintain confidence and self-esteem
- act to alleviate people's loneliness and isolation.

**Further information**

*Futures debate paper 2: Compassion in healthcare – the missing dimension of healthcare reform?*, NHS Confederation, May 2008.

www.dignityincare.org.uk

Each trust is required to obtain feedback from its own patients about their experiences of care. These surveys are intended to:

- track changes in patients' experience at trusts, year on year
- provide information for local quality improvement initiatives
- inform each trust's performance ratings and the performance indicators.

The DH launched the GP patient survey in 2006, which asked patients about their experiences of access and choice in primary care. The survey is now conducted annually and will eventually be carried out quarterly. For 2008/09 it was expanded, and 5.5 million patients were invited to take part.

Patients may also rate the service they received in hospital using the NHS Choices website. They are asked to comment on:

- dignity and respect
- cleanliness
- whether doctors and nurses worked well together
- if they felt they were involved in decisions about their care
- if they would recommend the hospital to friends and family.

### Further information

*GP patient survey: summary report 2007/2008 (England)*, Information Centre for Health and Social Care, 2008.
*National survey of adult inpatients 2007*, Healthcare Commission, May 2008.
NHS Surveys **www.nhssurveys.org**

### Performance regime

From 2009 a new performance regime will replace the system of 'annual health checks' operated by the former Healthcare Commission. The Care Quality Commission will instead carry out periodic reviews of NHS organisations. Providers will be assessed against core standards, national priorities, financial management and their use of the Mental Health Act and Mental Capacity Act. Commissioners will be judged using the world-class commissioning assurance system and 'vital signs' indicators (see page 42).

The DH intends the NHS performance regime to be consistent and transparent in identifying underperformance, supporting recovery and managing failure.

Key text: *State of healthcare report*

Before it was replaced by the Care Quality Commission, the Healthcare Commission produced every year an independent report to Parliament on the state of healthcare in England and Wales.

The final edition, published in December 2008, found:
- the NHS had benefited from funding increases and now has more resources than ever
- demand for care has risen dramatically
- the nation's health is improving
- improvements in meeting Government standards and targets have been sustained, with dramatic improvement in waiting times
- a few trusts are trapped at an unacceptably poor level of performance
- services are not always as patient-centred as they should be and certain groups' needs are not sufficiently well served
- safety of care is higher up the NHS agenda but trusts are still not doing enough to monitor and learn from incidents and ensure good practice is followed
- commissioning must improve, as must measurement of patient outcomes, patients' experience and the journey they make through the system.

## Roles and responsibilities within the NHS performance regime

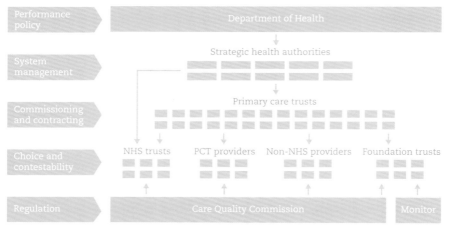

Source: Department of Health

The new performance regime's main features are:
- new minimum standards of quality, safety and financial management – trusts failing to meet these criteria will be identified as 'challenged'
- all challenged trusts will have to agree performance improvement plans with strategic health authorities, involving defined time periods and milestones against which improvement will be assessed
- in trusts unable to improve their performance in time, the management team may be replaced by one from elsewhere in the NHS, a foundation trust or the private sector.

The DH is developing an SHA assurance system, setting clear expectations of their roles and responsibilities and defining criteria for success, to be implemented in 2009/10.

The Next Stage Review recommended a national quality framework to enable the NHS to publish comparable information on key measures. It is under development, beginning with acute services and to be followed by community services. NHS organisations are being encouraged to develop their own quality frameworks combining national indicators with those appropriate locally.

### Further information
*Developing the NHS performance regime*, DH, June 2008.
*The regime for unsustainable NHS providers: response to consultation*, DH, January 2009.

# Ensuring patient safety

The NHS's first priority is its patients' safety. No healthcare system can be entirely risk-free but it must do everything possible to minimise unintended harm, whether from healthcare-associated infections or medical accidents. Failure to do so rapidly undermines public confidence in the system.

## Combating healthcare-associated infections

HCAIs are infections acquired in hospitals or as a result of healthcare interventions. They are caused by a wide variety of micro-organisms, often by bacteria that normally live harmlessly in or on the body. While HCAIs are most likely to be acquired during treatment in acute hospitals, they can also occur in GP surgeries, care homes, mental health trusts, ambulances and at home. They can have severe consequences for patients as well as costs for the NHS. An HCAI adds on average three to ten days to a patient's stay in hospital and costs between £4,000 and £10,000 to treat.

HCAIs are a worldwide problem. Since the mid-1980s, prevalence in hospitals worldwide has been 5 to 10 per cent; in England it is 8.2 per cent. For most patients, the risk of acquiring an infection is low (one case per 1,450 admissions for MRSA), and lower still for those who spend only one or two days in hospital.

Despite overall prevalence of HCAI remaining relatively constant during the last 25 years, the organisms themselves have changed, with new strains developing and others being controlled. The NHS faces particular problems with MRSA and *C. difficile*. MRSA can infect surgical wounds and ulcers, and if it enters the bloodstream can cause chest infections. It is usually spread through skin-to-skin contact, or by touching materials and surfaces contaminated from someone infected with MRSA. Measures such as hand washing and using alcohol handrub can help reduce the spread, as can isolating infected patients.

Toxins released by *C. difficile* cause diarrhoea, which can be severe and life-threatening. In most cases, the infection develops after cross-infection from another patient. Over 80 per cent of cases occur in people aged over 65. Alcohol handrubs are ineffective for *C. difficile*. Isolation of infected patients coupled with thorough hand-washing before and after contact, use of gloves and aprons and cleaning the ward are usually successful in prevention and control.

The NHS has two national targets to reduce HCAIs:
- maintaining the annual number of MRSA bloodstream infections at less than half the 2003/04 number
- reducing the number of C. *difficile* cases by 30 per cent nationally by 2011 compared to 2007/08.

Figures from the Health Protection Agency show that by September 2008 the number of MRSA infections had fallen by 57 per cent compared to 2003/04. Figures since then show the downward trend continuing. Cases of C. *difficile* infections had dropped by 33 per cent on the same quarter in 2007. Overall, figures show a 35.5 per cent decrease on the 2007/08 average.

The Government's HCAI and cleanliness strategy involves a wide range of measures to tackle HCAI, including:
- investing £270 million a year by 2010/11 in infection prevention and control and improving cleanliness
- encouraging hospitals to employ two infection control nurses, two isolation nurses and an anti-microbial pharmacist
- all non-emergency patients admitted to hospital are now screened for MRSA, and all emergency patients will be screened within three years
- annual infection control inspections of all acute trusts by specialist inspectors
- a bare-below-the-elbows dress code for hospital staff
- every hospital underwent a deep clean by March 2008
- a hygiene code contained in the Health Act 2006, stipulating that all trusts must establish appropriate systems, assess and manage risks, implement clinical care protocols, ensure healthcare workers' access to occupational health services and provide induction and training
- matrons have powers to report safety concerns direct to the Care Quality Commission
- a National Patient Safety Forum to set the agenda and check progress
- patient safety action teams in all strategic health authorities
- a patient safety charter agreed and signed by over 20 organisations
- a national 'cleanyourhands' campaign run by the NPSA since 2004, to which every acute trust has signed up and now extended to primary care, mental health, ambulance trusts and the independent sector.

An HCAI technology programme has been designed to accelerate development and adoption of new technologies to help fight infection. It includes the Showcase Hospitals scheme, comprising seven hospitals that trial innovative products to reduce and prevent HCAI. As part of a Design

Bugs Out project, designers have been challenged to devise new furniture, equipment and services for hospital wards that will enhance cleanliness.

However, Healthcare Commission spot checks in 2008 of 51 NHS trusts – 30 per cent of the acute sector – found only five totally compliant with the hygiene code and 27 failing to keep all areas clean and well maintained. While 97 per cent of lapses did not pose an immediate risk to patient safety, the commission suggested almost all acute trusts have more work to do.

**Further information**
*Code of practice for the prevention and control of health care associated infections*, DH, October 2006.
*Going further faster II: applying the learning to reduce HCAI and improve cleanliness*, DH, June 2008.
*From deep clean to keep clean: learning from the deep clean programme*, DH, October 2008.
**www.clean-safe-care.nhs.uk**

Key texts

### An organisation with a memory
Compiled by an expert group led by the chief medical officer (CMO) and published in June 2000, this recommended a mandatory reporting scheme for adverse healthcare events and near-misses. It set out to encourage a reporting and questioning culture in the NHS to replace blame with a proper understanding of the underlying causes of failures.

### Winning ways
Launched by the CMO in December 2003, this required chief executives to ensure that infection control teams work with bed managers to optimise bed use, while implementing procedures to minimise the risk of infection.

### Safety first – a report for patients, clinicians and healthcare managers
Commissioned by the CMO and published in December 2006, this updated progress since *An organisation with a memory* and said more remains to be done to ensure patient safety. Its recommendations included a patient safety forum, refocusing the National Patient Safety Agency's role, setting up local patient safety action teams and ensuring national priorities take explicit account of patient safety from 2008.

**National Patient Safety Agency**

NPSA is responsible for promoting patient safety throughout the UK wherever the NHS provides care. NHS staff anonymously report incidents that did or could have affected patient safety to NPSA.

NPSA has three divisions:

**National Reporting and Learning Service** – collects, analyses and prioritises data on patient safety incidents in the NHS, making recommendations to reduce risk. In the year to March 2008, there were 959,590 incidents reported, most causing no harm but 3,471 reported to have caused death.

**National Clinical Assessment Service** – provides confidential advice and support where the performance of doctors and dentists is causing concern. Employing organisations, managers or practitioners themselves can contact NCAS for advice. The service also covers the independent sector.

**National Research Ethics Service** – promotes ethical research to maintain a review system that protects the safety, dignity and well-being of research participants. It provides support for research ethics committees that assess and oversee research projects.

NPSA commissions and monitors the three national confidential inquiries into patient outcome and death, maternal and child health, and suicide and homicide by mentally ill people.

**Further information**
*Briefing 161: Act on reporting: five actions to improve patient safety reporting,*
NHS Confederation/NPSA, June 2008.
*Large scale workforce change: Briefing 51: Improving patient safety and information governance,* NHS Employers, November 2008.
www.npsa.nhs.uk

## Reforming clinical negligence procedures

Although the NHS provides high-quality healthcare for millions of people every year, occasionally patients do not receive the treatment they should, or mistakes are made. In the UK and other developed countries, about 10 per cent of hospital admissions may result in some kind of adverse event, and a third of these patients will suffer severe illness or die. In NHS primary care, research suggests about 600 errors a day occur, mainly in diagnosis and treatment, of which a fifth will cause harm.

Anyone who suffers harm as a result of treatment must receive an apology, a clear explanation of what went wrong, proper treatment and care and, where appropriate, financial compensation. The NHS must ensure it learns from such experiences.

But legal proceedings for medical injury are slow, complex and costly. They divert clinical staff from providing care, and can damage morale as well as public confidence. The system encourages defensiveness and secrecy, which hampers the NHS from learning and improvement. Under the NHS Redress Act 2006, a scheme to be implemented from 2009/10 provides an alternative to litigation for less severe cases. The Government hopes that the scheme will shift emphasis from attributing blame towards preventing harm, reducing risks and learning from mistakes. It does not fundamentally alter the existing legal system but provides an additional mechanism.

The intention is that the scheme should deal with claims under £20,000, avoiding the courts altogether; if a patient accepts compensation under the scheme, they will be barred from taking legal proceedings. Compensation is intended to be roughly equal to what a court might order. The Act applies only to NHS hospital care and excludes GP practices, dental surgeries and private healthcare. The NHS Litigation Authority will decide liability and compensation, as well as instituting and investigating claims. The scheme does not include an appeals process, but if a patient is dissatisfied with the outcome, they may begin legal proceedings.

The Act applies to England and contains framework powers for Wales only. The scheme cannot apply in Scotland or Northern Ireland.

### Further information
*NHS redress: improving the response to patients*, DH, October 2005.
*NHS redress: statement of policy*, DH, November 2005.

**Spotlight on policy: 'Never events'**

'Never events' are serious and largely preventable patient safety incidents. Originally a US concept, they were highlighted by the Next Stage Review as another way for the NHS to raise quality. The NPSA drew up a list of never events for the NHS:

- wrong-site surgery
- retained instrument post-operation
- wrong route administration of chemotherapy
- misplaced naso or orogastric tube not detected before use
- inpatient suicide using non-collapsible rails or while on one-to-one observation
- transferred prisoners absconding from medium- or high-secure mental health services
- in-hospital maternal death from post-partum haemorrhage after elective caesarean
- intravenous administration of mis-selected concentrated potassium chloride.

PCTs may use this set as part of their contract agreements with providers. It is proposed to link never events to payment regimes from 2010/11. PCTs will monitor their occurrence in services they commission, reporting them to the NPSA and to the public.

**Key organisation: NHS Litigation Authority**

NHSLA, set up in 1995, handles negligence claims against NHS bodies in England, and operates a risk management programme to help raise standards and reduce incidents leading to claims. It also monitors human rights case law and co-ordinates equal-pay claims on the NHS's behalf.

In 2007/08 NHSLA received 5,470 claims for clinical negligence and paid out £661 million in damages and costs. At March 2008 it had 16,959 live claims. Fewer than 50 clinical negligence cases a year are contested in court, and 96 per cent of the NHSLA's cases are settled out of court. Claims are settled on average in a year and a half. Of all clinical claims handled since 1997:
- 41 per cent were abandoned by the claimant
- 42 per cent were settled out of court
- 4 per cent were settled in court
- 13 per cent are outstanding.
www.nhsla.com

THE **NHS** CONFEDERATION

*"Excellent events and most valuable networking opportunities"*
David Cox, Chair, South Birmingham PCT

# High-quality events for health leaders

The NHS Confederation runs a range of high-quality events designed to meet the needs of senior health leaders across the service.

- Hear from influential speakers
- Get beneath the surface of the key issues
- Engage with colleagues and develop your contacts

Visit the website for more information and to sign up for our events newsletter.
**www.nhsconfed.org/events**

# 06 Accountability and regulation

Primary care trusts and NHS trusts are accountable outwards to their local communities and upwards through their strategic health authority to the Department of Health, which in turn is accountable through its ministers to Parliament and the electorate. NHS organisations must demonstrate strategic and operational accountability: they must have a clear and well-evidenced long-term plan, and show transparency in their day-to-day decisions. They are accountable to local people who are consumers of their services and taxpayers who fund the NHS: therefore, they have a duty to maintain the highest standards of quality and safety, as well as to balance the books and provide value for money.

NHS organisations are immediately accountable to independently appointed boards, and they have a duty to involve and consult patients and the public. They can also be called to account by their local authority, and must answer to a variety of national regulators and inspectorates. The healthcare professions too are subject to their own regulatory bodies, which set standards and police them.

## The role of boards

### Duties and responsibilities

NHS boards' roles and responsibilities are broadly the same throughout the UK. They take corporate responsibility for their organisation's strategies and actions. With the Next Stage Review's emphasis on decentralisation, local leadership and autonomy, their role will become more important than ever.

Boards generally consist of five executives (including the chief executive and finance director) and five non-executives plus a chair. The chair and non-executives are lay people drawn from the local community, and are accountable to the Secretary of State.

A board's main duties are:
- collective responsibility for adding value to the organisation by promoting its success through direction and supervision of its affairs
- providing active leadership within a framework of prudent and effective controls which enable risk to be assessed and managed
- setting the organisation's strategic aims, ensuring the necessary financial and human resources are in place for it to meet its objectives and reviewing management performance

- setting and maintaining the organisation's values and standards, while ensuring its obligations to patients, the local community and the Secretary of State are understood and met.

Legally, there is no distinction between the board duties of executive and non-executive directors: they both share responsibility for the organisation's direction and control. The board is expected to bring about change by making best use of all its resources – financial, staffing, physical infrastructure and knowledge – and working with staff and partner organisations to meet the public's and patients' expectations. As leaders, board members are expected to understand opportunities for improving services and motivate others to bring them about.

Boards make plans to achieve the Government's objectives for healthcare, guided by long-term strategy such as the Next Stage Review's recommendations and shorter-term aims such as the NHS's operating framework. Boards have increasing scope to pace their plans to reflect local circumstances, and have a large say over how to achieve them – in theory at least. All boards sign off an annual business plan setting out the year's objectives, and it is the whole board's function to ensure progress.

NHS boards are obliged to ensure their organisations have an ethos and culture of public service that reflects and respects public expectation. The need for public accountability means boards must conduct business in an open and transparent way that commands public confidence. Their meetings are open to the public, and should be understandable to the public.

On rare occasions it is necessary to remove a chair or non-executive from their post if they prove unable to meet the requirements of public office. The Appointments Commission has the power to terminate appointments but not to suspend them – for example, while an allegation was investigated. The DH has consulted on a proposal to introduce such a power.

### Further information
*Governing the NHS: A guide for boards*, DH and Appointments Commission, June 2003.
*Codes of conduct and accountability for NHS boards*, Appointments Commission/DH, July 2004.
*Adding value to a 21st century health service: a review of the NHS public appointments process*, Appointments Commission, November 2007.
*Removing or suspending chairs and non-executives of PCTs and NHS trusts from office: feedback on the consultation to introduce powers of suspension*, DH, May 2008.

**Is accountability adequate?**

Local accountability and the need to strengthen the transparency of decision-making in the NHS are hot political topics. Unprecedented investment in health coupled with high-profile reports of failures in some NHS organisations have led to a feeling among the political parties that local decision-making needs to be more transparent. Reconfiguration controversies – despite no major hospital closing since 1997 – have spawned the belief that existing accountability mechanisms are not sufficiently robust for PCTs to demonstrate a mandate for major service changes such as closing emergency departments. The NHS Constitution (see page 115) and the commissioning assurance framework (see page 43) are both attempts to strengthen accountability.

Options for improving PCT accountability might include adopting a membership scheme similar to that for foundation trusts, directly electing all or some board non-executives (as is proposed in Scotland, see page 233) or appointing local authority members to boards on a quota basis. Responsibility for commissioning could be transferred to local government, or new bodies could be created to sit between the NHS and local authorities. Whatever the model, it would need to be:
• clear, accessible and transparent
• inclusive
• responsive
• sustainable
• proactive
• able to make difficult decisions
• cost-effective
• able to reduce health inequalities.

**Further information**
*Principles for accountability; putting the public at the heart of the NHS*, PCTN/NHS Confederation, January 2008.
*Discussion paper 2: The development of membership schemes for PCTs – a legitimate response*, PCTN/NHS Confederation, September 2008.

### The chair
In 2003 the Higgs Report laid out the responsibilities and expectations of chairs and non-executives. Although the report looked at commercial enterprises, its principles are relevant to all NHS boards. As identified by

the Higgs Report and modified to reflect the NHS, a chair's main role is:
- leadership of the board, ensuring its effectiveness in all aspects of its role and setting its agenda
- ensuring provision of accurate, timely and clear information to directors
- ensuring effective communication with staff, patients and the public
- arranging regular evaluation of the board's performance, its committees and individual directors
- helping non-executive directors contribute effectively and ensuring constructive relations between executive and non-executive directors.

In general, a strong correlation exists between the quality of the chair's and chief executive's leadership and the organisation's success. Where an organisation is not delivering, questions can legitimately be asked about the quality of the board leadership.

### Non-executive directors
The Higgs Report said that non-executives should:
- constructively challenge and contribute to developing strategy, scrutinise managers' performance in meeting objectives and monitor the reporting of performance
- satisfy themselves that financial information is accurate and that financial controls and risk management are robust
- be responsible for deciding executive directors' pay, as well as have a prime role in appointing – and where necessary, removing – senior managers and in succession planning
- ensure the board acts in the public's best interests and is fully accountable to it for the organisation's services and the public funds it uses.

Remuneration for chairs and non-executives

|  | Chairs | Non executives | Audit committee chairs |
|---|---|---|---|
| Strategic health authorities | £41,411–£62,117 | £7,765 | £12,941 |
| Primary care trusts | £31,059–£41,411 | £7,765 | £12,941 |
| NHS trusts | £18,164–£23,020 | £6,005 | £6,005 |

Source: Appointments Commission

There are about 3,000 chairs and non-executives in NHS organisations in England, excluding foundation trusts. During 2007/08, these were 898 appointments and re-appointments made. Women make up 35.7 per cent of all appointments, while people from black and minority ethnic groups account for 11.9 per cent. Non-executives work two-and-a-half days a month, while chairs work three to three-and-a-half days a week.

Foundation trusts set their own rates, which are generally much higher than other NHS organisations.

### Further information
*Review of the roles and effectiveness of non-executive directors (Higgs Report)*, DTI, January 2003.

## The chief executive
The chief executive is responsible for ensuring the board is empowered to govern the organisation and its objectives are accomplished through effective and properly controlled executive action. A chief executive's main responsibilities are:
• leadership
• delivery planning
• performance management
• governance
• accountability.

## Board committees
NHS boards may delegate some of their powers to formally constituted committees. Some are set up to advise the board on a permanent basis, such as the:
• audit committee
• remuneration and terms of service committee
• clinical governance committee
• risk management committee.

## PCT boards and PECs
Like other NHS organisations, PCTs are overseen by a board consisting of a lay chair and a majority of non-executives, although they must include a director of public health. In addition, to reflect the importance of clinical leadership in PCTs, each has a professional executive committee (PEC), which may include GPs, nurses, social workers, allied health professionals, dentists, pharmacists, optometrists and consultants; clinicians must be in

a majority but PECs should not be dominated by one professional group. Since 2007 PCTs have been free to decide how many members their PEC has and how much it pays them, based on guiding principles from the DH.

PECs are responsible for guiding the PCT board through detailed thinking on priorities, service policies and investment plans.

**Further information**
*Fit for the future*, DH, March 2007.

## Foundation trust boards

Foundation trusts have distinctive governance arrangements to reflect their freedom from central control. Staff, patients and local people are eligible to become 'members' of the trust. Membership entitles them to vote at elections for the board of governors and to stand for election to the board. According to Monitor, foundation trusts had recruited over 1.2 million members by the end of 2008. The Prime Minister has said he wants 3 million foundation trust members by 2012.

The board of governors will include those elected by the trust members and staff, as well as people appointed by PCTs and local authorities. Representatives elected by patients and the public must be in the majority, while at least three must be elected by staff. The board of governors' role is to advise the board of directors on its forward plans.

Each foundation trust has a board of directors made up of non-executives appointed by the governors and executive directors appointed by the non-executives, similar to other NHS organisations. This board is responsible for managing the foundation trust, including its day-to-day operation and forward business plan.

Board of directors' meetings concern the trust's operational business, with board of governors' meetings focusing more on members' needs and ensuring local communities can contribute to decision-making.

**Further information**
*New voices, new accountabilities: a guide to foundation trust wider governance*, Foundation Trust Network, August 2005.
*Membership governance in NHS foundation trusts: a review for the Department of Health*, University of Birmingham/Mutuo, March 2008.
*Developing the role of NHS foundation trust governors*, Monitor, June 2008.

**Key organisation: Appointments Commission**

The Appointments Commission is the independent organisation responsible on behalf of ministers for appointing chairs and non-executives to strategic health authorities, primary care trusts, NHS trusts and the Department of Health's arm's length bodies. It also provides non-executive recruitment services for foundation trusts and to the boards of public bodies across central government.

The Commission:

- manages the recruitment, selection and appointment of chairs and non-executive directors
- provides year-long induction training for chairs and non-executives, ensuring the best possible start for new appointees
- acts as the 'guardian' of the appraisal process, setting minimum standards and providing guidance and advice
- promotes good governance through advice, guidance and policy development
- provides support and advice to the chairs via regionally based commissioners.

For foundation trusts the Commission can offer a range of recruitment services, including professional pre-assessment, stakeholder involvement sessions, arranging psychometric testing and assessment exercises and induction training. The Commission also works with aspirant foundation trusts to help them strengthen their boards – in particular identifying candidates with the appropriate financial and commercial skills.
**www.appointments.org.uk**

## Engaging patients and the public

Engaging patients and the public in health services can be interpreted in different ways.

- Individual patients may be involved together with health professionals in making decisions about their own care.
- Organisations may seek direct feedback from patients about their experiences of using services.
- Users of a particular service may be involved as a group in advising how it might be improved.
- Members of the public may be involved in making strategic decisions about how or where services are to be provided.

Since the NHS Plan of 2000, the health service has had an explicit duty to ensure patients and the public have a real say in how services are planned and developed. The NHS Act 2006 places a duty on strategic health authorities, primary care trusts, NHS trusts and foundation trusts to 'involve and consult' patients and the public. They were already required by law to consult on substantial variations and developments to services; under the Act, they must arrange to involve and consult patients and the public in:

• planning and provision of services they are responsible for
• developing and considering proposals for changes in the way those services are provided
• decisions to be made that affect how those services operate.

Under the Local Government and Public Involvement in Health Act 2007, strategic health authorities, PCTs, NHS trusts and foundation trusts have a strengthened duty to involve service users or their representatives. This came into force in November 2008. In addition, a new 'duty to report on consultation' will apply to PCTs and SHAs from October 2009, which requires them to report on how people's views have shaped the decisions they make when commissioning services.

The NHS Constitution establishes as an underlying principle that the health service will involve individual patients and the wider community, and be accountable to the public, communities and patients. It includes specific rights for patients to be involved in discussions and decisions about their healthcare, in planning healthcare services and in decisions about proposed changes and how services are run. The NHS also pledges to provide the information needed to enable this to happen.

PCTs are expected to 'proactively seek and build continuous and meaningful engagement with the public and patients to shape services and improve health' as part of the world-class commissioning assurance framework (see page 43). From April 2009, comprehensive area assessments (see page 55) will add further impetus to effective engagement by judging how people are served by their local public services and how these address the local community's priorities.

**Human rights and healthcare**

Human rights are based on the 'FREDA' values of fairness, respect, equality, dignity and autonomy. The Government has incorporated into UK law most of the rights defined in the European Convention through the Human Rights Act 1998. This was intended to bring about a culture of human rights in public services. Putting human rights at the heart of how health services are designed and delivered can improve experience and outcomes for patients and staff. It also supports the Next Stage Review's aspirations for a personalised service.

The Act provides a framework that can help NHS organisations ensure individuals receive fair, dignified and equitable treatment. Of the 15 rights defined in the Act, most relevant to healthcare are the rights:
• not to be treated in an inhuman or degrading way
• to respect for private and family life, home and correspondence
• to liberty and the right to life
• not to be discriminated against.

Examples of human rights issues in practice include 'do not resuscitate' orders, unsanitary conditions, excessive force in restraint, staff disciplinary procedures, privacy on wards and family visits. NHS organisations can take a human rights-based approach by ensuring accountability and empowerment, by encouraging participation and involvement and by paying attention to vulnerable groups, ensuring they are not discriminated against.

**Further information**
*Human rights in healthcare – a short introduction*, DH, October 2008.
*Human rights in healthcare – a framework for local action*, DH, October 2008.

All this means discussing with patients and the public their ideas, the organisation's plans, patients' experiences, why services need to change, what people want from services and how to make best use of resources. Boards must consider patient and public involvement (PPI) issues on their agendas, include among their membership an individual to champion these issues and designate a staff member responsible for the activity. They must commit resources to patient and public involvement, and ensure all staff are trained in it.

Since the NHS Plan, every trust has had to obtain feedback from patients about their experiences of care. Information from patient surveys is used in assessing trusts' performance. Many acute trusts and other service providers are seeking direct patient feedback, including 'real-time' feedback, to improve their understanding of people's experiences of care.

Since April 2008, new PPI bodies, local involvement networks, have been established in every PCT/local social care authority (see below). In addition, local authority overview and scrutiny committees (see page 160) are intended to ensure elected councillors have a say in the NHS in their area, while the public can become members of foundation trusts and elect representatives to the board of governors (see page 147).

### Further information
*Real involvement: working with people to improve services*, DH, October 2008.
*Involving people and communities: a brief guide to the NHS duties to involve and report on consultation*, DH, October 2008.

### Local Involvement Networks (LINks)
In 2008, 150 LINks replaced 400 patient and public involvement forums (PPIFs) as the main vehicles for involving patients and the public in the NHS. LINks cover all publicly funded health and social care services in a local authority area, irrespective of who provides them. They have the power to investigate concerns, demand information, enter and view services, make reports and recommendations and refer issues to local councillors on overview and scrutiny committees (see page 160) – which have the power to summon NHS managers.

LINks are made up of individuals, groups and organisations with an interest in local services, although they do not have to adopt a particular structure. They:
• help commissioners understand the services people want to receive
• monitor services
• provide a means for the NHS and social care to reach out to their communities and seek their views.

Each LINk is supported and guided by a host organisation contracted by the local authority. The Government has earmarked £84 million over three years for setting up LINks, most of which will go to local authorities.

## Membership of a LINk

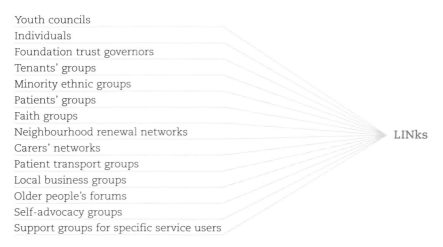

Youth councils
Individuals
Foundation trust governors
Tenants' groups
Minority ethnic groups
Patients' groups
Faith groups
Neighbourhood renewal networks
Carers' networks
Patient transport groups
Local business groups
Older people's forums
Self-advocacy groups
Support groups for specific service users

LINks

Source: Department of Health

PPIFs, set up in 2003, related to specific organisations rather than entire geographical areas, and did not cover social care. It is intended that LINks will involve many more people and work more closely with the voluntary sector than PPIFs. Before the advent of PPIFs, community health councils acted as patient and public representatives in England until they were abolished in 2003. They continue in Wales with new powers. NHSScotland has replaced its local health councils with a single Scottish Health Council that has local offices in each board area, while Northern Ireland has replaced its four health and social service councils with a single Patient and Client Council.

### Further information

*What you said: response to the consultation on regulations for local involvement networks (LINks)*, DH, August 2008.
*Listening and responding to communities: a brief guide to local involvement networks*, DH, September 2008.
**www.dh.gov.uk/links**
**www.direct.gov.uk/localinvolvementnetworks**

### Patient advice and liaison services

Every NHS trust and PCT should have a patient advice and liaison service
(PALS) providing on-the-spot help and information about health services.
PALS aim to:

- resolve concerns before they become major problems
- provide information to patients, carers and their families about local
  health services and put people in contact with local support groups
- tell people about the complaints procedure and independent complaints
  advocacy support
- act as an early-warning system by monitoring trends, highlighting gaps
  in service and making reports for action to trust managers.

The National PALS Network aims to promote PALS and support the
professional development of PALS staff, as well as acting as a national
voice for the service.

### Further information

*National evaluation of PALS: briefing for chief executives*, University of the West of
England/DH, September 2006.

www.pals.nhs.uk

# Complaints

### Reforming complaints procedures

Since April 2009, a single complaints system has existed for all health
and local authority adult social care services in England. The new unified
arrangements aim to:

- resolve complaints locally in a more personal and flexible way
- ensure early and effective resolution and robust handling of all cases,
  not just the more complex
- make sure people with complaints have access to effective support,
  particularly those who find it difficult to make their views heard
- give people the option of going direct to their PCT with a complaint
  about their GP, NHS dentist or pharmacist instead of complaining
  directly to the practice
- give people the option of going direct to their local authority where their
  care has been arranged by the local authority
- ensure organisations improve services by routinely learning from
  people's experiences.

The range of measures available locally to resolve complaints include:

- robust risk assessment to deal quickly with serious complaints, such as
  those involving abuse or unsafe practice
- a plan, agreed by the complainant, outlining how the complaint is going
  to be tackled, who will be involved and their roles, timescales and how
  the complainant will be kept informed of progress
- involvement of the most senior managers or clinicians at an early stage
  where appropriate
- early face-to-face meetings between everyone concerned to make sure
  the circumstances giving rise to the complaint are clearly understood
- independent mediators when the complaint includes relationships that
  have broken down

- people independent of the service provider, commissioning organisation or the locality to investigate where complaints cannot be resolved satisfactorily or complex issues are involved
- specialist advocates to help people with complex needs voice their complaint effectively and understand the organisation's response
- clear, effective leadership from the most senior managers to ensure complaints arrangements meet people's needs and services are improved as a result.

The Ombudsman's role (see page 159) remains unchanged in order to maintain an ultimate, independent view of what has happened.

In 2007/08, NHS trusts received 87,080 complaints, a 4 per cent decrease on the previous year. Three out of four were resolved locally within 25 days. Complaints included:
- 35,159 about all aspects of clinical care
- 11,844 about delays and cancellations of appointments
- 10,908 about the attitude of staff.

Complaints about primary care totalled 43,942, a 3 per cent increase on the previous year.

### Further information
*Making experiences count: a new approach to responding to complaints*, DH, June 2007.
*Feeding back? Learning from complaints handling in health and social care*, National Audit Office, October 2008.
*Reform of health and social care complaints: proposed changes to the legislative framework*, DH, December 2008.
*Spotlight on complaints 2009: a report on second-stage complaints about the NHS in England*, Healthcare Commission, February 2009.
*Listening, responding, improving: a guide to better customer care*, DH, February 2009.

## Independent Complaints Advocacy Services (ICAS)

ICAS are available across the country to help individuals pursue complaints about the NHS. Complainants can contact their local ICAS office direct, or through complaints managers at hospitals, PCTs and GP practices, NHS Direct or the patient advice and liaison service (PALS). ICAS aims to ensure complainants have access to the support they need to articulate their concerns and navigate the complaints system. It can simply offer advice or write letters and attend meetings to speak on the complainant's behalf. Since 2006 three independent organisations with experience of advocacy have delivered ICAS under contract across England.

**Further information**
*The first year of ICAS: 1 September 2003–31 August 2004*, DH, January 2005.

Spotlight on policy: **Freedom of information**
The Freedom of Information Act 2000 requires every public authority to adopt a 'publication scheme' that specifies the classes of information the authority publishes, the form it takes and whether it charges for the information. Each scheme must be approved by the Information Commissioner, an independent public official responsible for overseeing operation of the Act, who also has powers of enforcement.

Since January 2005, NHS organisations must answer requests for information within the terms of the individual right of access given by the Act. This applies to all types of recorded information held by the organisation regardless of its date, although the Act specifies some exemptions – such as information where the patient is identifiable. Anyone making a request must be told whether the organisation holds the information and, if so, be supplied with it – generally within 20 working days. Organisations also have a duty to provide advice or help to anyone seeking information. Where a request for information is denied, it may be possible to appeal against the decision.

**Further information**
*Freedom of Information publication scheme – guide to information*, DH, December 2008.
Information Commissioner **www.ico.gov.uk**
**www.foi.nhs.uk**

# Regulation and inspection

NHS organisations and the healthcare professions are all subject to stringent regulation, audit and inspection to ensure they maintain high service standards and provide value for money.

## The regulators

Many national bodies are responsible for regulating, auditing and inspecting various aspects of NHS services – some long-established, others more recently set up as the Government's reform agenda has progressed. This has led to NHS organisations feeling overburdened by the demands of different regulatory authorities, in particular preparing for numerous inspections by different bodies and dealing with broadly similar information requests in different formats or covering different time periods. The NHS Confederation has identified 50 bodies inspecting trusts.

In response the Government has pledged to reduce the number and improve the co-ordination of data requests to those on the front line of healthcare. The Healthcare Concordat was launched in 2004 for this purpose, and 20 of the main bodies that inspect the NHS and adult social care signed it. In 2007, the Government set a target to reduce the data burden from central departments on frontline staff by 30 per cent by 2010. The Information Centre (see page 225) is pursuing further initiatives to streamline data collection requests. In 2009 the Care Quality Commission replaced the Healthcare Commission, Commission for Social Care Inspection and Mental Health Act Commission, to provide 'joined-up' regulation of health and social care for the first time.

## Further information

*The bureaucratic burden in the NHS, NHS Confederation*, March 2007
*Review of health and social care burdens final report – recommendations,* Lifting the Burdens Taskforce/Local Government Association, September 2008.
*Simplification plan: year three*, DH, December 2008.

The following are among the major national bodies regulating and inspecting the NHS:

## Care Quality Commission

Beginning work in April 2009, the CQC functions across both health and social care, reflecting closer integration between the two. Its functions are:

- assuring safety and quality
- assessing commissioners' and providers' performance
- monitoring how the Mental Health Act is working
- managing and co-ordinating regulation and inspection across health and adult social care.

In its first year, the CQC will begin registration of NHS trusts and assess them in relation to healthcare associated infections. This will be a transitional year as the CQC brings together the regulatory regimes of its processor bodies to develop an integrated regulatory framework.

In 2010 health and social care providers will be required to register with the new regulator in order to provide services (see page 161). The commission has a wide range of enforcement powers to achieve compliance with registration requirements, including those relating to infection control. It can apply specific conditions to respond to specific risks – such as requiring a ward or service to be closed until safety requirements are met – as well as being able to suspend or de-register services where absolutely necessary.
www.cqc.org.uk

## Monitor

Established in 2004, Monitor authorises and regulates NHS foundation trusts. It receives and considers applications from NHS trusts, and if satisfied that they meet its criteria, grants them foundation status. Once established, it monitors their activities to ensure they comply with their terms of authorisation. Monitor has power to intervene in the running of a foundation trust in the event of failings in its healthcare standards or other aspects of its activities. It is independent of the Government and directly accountable to Parliament.
www.monitor-nhsft.gov.uk

## National Institute for Health and Clinical Excellence (NICE)

Set up in 1999, NICE provides guidance in three areas:

- public health – promotion of good health and the prevention of ill health for those working in the NHS, local authorities and the wider public and voluntary sector

- health technologies – the use of new and existing medicines, treatments and procedures within the NHS
- clinical practice – the appropriate treatment and care of people with specific diseases and conditions within the NHS.

The DH commissions NICE to examine specific topics, which may be suggested by patients, the public, health professionals or the national clinical directors. Health professionals and the NHS are expected to take NICE guidance fully into account, although it does not override their responsibility to make appropriate decisions based on individual patients' circumstances. Local government and NHS organisations must take account of NICE public health guidance in working towards the targets in the *Choosing health* white paper (see page 56) and in local area agreements. The Next Stage Review recommended that all patients be guaranteed access to NICE-approved drugs if their doctor prescribes them. It also called for NICE to be expanded so it could set more independent quality standards, and for its appraisal process to be speeded up.

NICE's 30-strong citizens council keeps the organisation informed on what the public thinks about the use of treatments and NHS care. Members are drawn from all age groups, social circumstances, ethnic backgrounds, regions and abilities. NICE's partners council is appointed by the Secretary of State and meets annually to review the annual report. It includes patients and representatives of patient organisations, professional organisations and healthcare industries.
www.nice.org.uk

### The Ombudsman
The office of the Parliamentary and Health Service Ombudsman (sometimes referred to as the Health Service Commissioner) undertakes independent investigations into complaints about the NHS in England, as well as government departments and other public bodies. It is completely independent of the NHS and Government. In the NHS, the Ombudsman investigates complaints that a hardship or injustice has been caused by its failure to provide a service, by a failure in service or by maladministration. The Ombudsman looks into complaints against private health providers only if the treatment was funded by the NHS.

Complainants can only refer their cases to the Ombudsman after failing to achieve a resolution with the organisation or practitioner they are complaining against – for example, because of delays in dealing with a complaint locally or failure to get a satisfactory answer. The Ombudsman can consider complaints from a patient; a close member of the family, partner or representative, if the patient is unable to act for themselves; or from someone who has suffered injustice or hardship as a result of the actions of the NHS. A complaint will normally only be considered within a year of the events which gave rise to it.

The Ombudsman publishes detailed reports of investigations, which identify common themes in complaints. The reports are intended to be used as training tools to improve services, and chief executives are asked to ensure all clinical directors and complaints managers are aware of them. They are also considered by the House of Commons public administration committee.
www.ombudsman.org.uk

## Audit Commission
The Audit Commission is an independent public body responsible for ensuring that public money is spent economically, efficiently and effectively. As well as the NHS it covers local government, housing, criminal justice and fire and rescue services. In particular, it is dedicated to raising the standards of financial management and challenging public bodies to deliver better value for money.
www.audit-commission.gov.uk

## National Audit Office
Headed by the Comptroller and Auditor General, the NAO's role is to report direct to Parliament on how public bodies have spent central government money, conducting financial audits and assessing value for money. It works closely with the Commons public accounts committee.
www.nao.org.uk

## Overview and scrutiny committees (OSCs)
The Health and Social Care Act 2001 gave local authorities specific powers to scrutinise local health services and health organisations. These powers formally rest with authorities that have social care responsibilities (county, unitary, metropolitan, London borough authorities), but there are provisions for joint or delegated scrutiny with borough or district councils.

OSCs are made up of elected council members not on the authority's executive or cabinet. They are able to call chief executives of local health organisations to attend a scrutiny hearing at least twice a year. OSCs can:
- refer contested service changes to the Secretary of State
- report their recommendations locally
- insist on being consulted by the NHS over major changes to health services.

The Centre for Public Scrutiny helped to foster local authorities' role in scrutinising health services by running a support programme. It has published a guide for health OSCs, clarifying their distinct roles.

The Government intends to update policy on OSCs, and the Local Democracy, Economic Development and Construction Bill makes proposals to strengthen the powers.

### Further information
*Local authority health overview and scrutiny committees & patient and public involvement forums: working together – a practical guide*, CfPS, July 2005.
Centre for Public Scrutiny **www.cfps.org.uk**

### Spotlight on policy: Registration with CQC
From 2010 all health and social care providers of defined regulated activities will have to register with the Care Quality Commission. These activities include, for example, personal care, treatment of disease or injury and surgical procedures. Most independent health and social care providers currently registered with the CQC's predecessor bodies will have their registration transferred, while most NHS trusts, foundation trusts and PCT community services will need to register. Registration of primary medical and dental services is likely to be phased in. Some services are excluded from the scope of registration because they are already overseen by other legislation.

Registration will depend on the provider complying with legally enforceable standards of quality and safety. CQC has enforcement powers and sanctions to secure compliance, including powers to refuse or cancel registration.

### Further information
*Briefing 159: Future registration framework for health and social care*, NHS Confederation, May 2008.

# Professional regulation

NHS patients need to know that the staff who care for them are well trained and competent. Professional self-regulation has been a cornerstone of the NHS since it began, yet events over the last decade or so – such as the Bristol Inquiry into the deaths of child heart patients, the Alder Hey cases in which organs from dead children were retained without their families' knowledge, and Dr Harold Shipman's conviction for multiple murders – highlighted the need for reform.

Professional self-regulation covers education, registration, training, continuing professional development and revalidation. It includes setting standards for deciding who should enter and remain members of a profession and determining their fitness to practise. Its underpinning principles are:
• clarity about standards
• maintaining public confidence
• transparency in tackling fitness to practise
• responsiveness to and protection of patients.

## Professional regulatory bodies

The NHS Plan stipulated that regulatory bodies had to reform to become smaller, with much greater public and patient representation, faster, more transparent procedures and more meaningful accountability to the public and the health service. This was reinforced by the Kennedy Report on the Bristol Royal Infirmary Inquiry a year later (see page 154).

The Government has insisted that regulators develop common systems across the professions and agree standards that put patients' interests first. It is keen that self-regulation keeps pace with change in the NHS as well as society's attitudes and public opinion. Professional regulatory bodies must be open and make improvements based on feedback from patients, their representatives and the public. They must deal with complaints quickly, thoroughly, objectively and in a way that is responsive to the complainant while treating fairly the health professional complained against.

Updated regulatory bodies have been introduced for nursing, midwifery and health visiting and the allied health professions:
• **The Nursing and Midwifery Council** replaced the UK Central Council in 2002 as the body responsible for governing nurses, midwives and health visitors.

- **The Health Professions Council** is responsible for the professions previously regulated by the Council for Professions Supplementary to Medicine, and includes groups of healthcare professionals not previously covered by formal statutory regulation.
- **The Council for Healthcare Regulatory Excellence** (see opposite) scrutinises and oversees the nine statutory regulatory bodies for the health professions, working with them to identify and promote good practice in regulation, carrying out research, developing policy and giving advice.
- **The General Medical Council** is the regulatory body for doctors. It receives about 5,000 complaints a year, of which about 1,700 result in investigation.

### Further information
General Medical Council **www.gmc-uk.org**
Nursing and Midwifery Council **www.nmc-uk.org**
Health Professions Council **www.hpc-uk.org**

### Reforming professional regulation
Following the Shipman Inquiry, the chief medical officer reviewed the regulation of the medical profession, and a parallel review of non-medical professional regulation also took place. The Government subsequently published its proposals in a white paper, *Trust, assurance and safety: the regulation of health professionals in the 21st century*, now being implemented. Key changes include:
- measures to make regulators more independent, such as professional members no longer forming the majority on regulatory bodies, and an independent adjudicator for doctors
- measures to ensure healthcare professionals are objectively revalidated throughout their career and remain up-to-date with clinical best practice
- moving from the criminal standard of proof to the civil standard with a sliding scale in fitness-to-practise cases
- a stronger role for the medical Royal Colleges
- introducing a system of regional GMC affiliates who will help local employers address concerns about doctors
- establishment of a General Pharmaceutical Council from 2010
- developing a comprehensive strategy for prevention, treatment and rehabilitation services for all health professionals.

CHRE is a statutory body responsible to Parliament and independent of the Department of Health. It covers all the UK, promoting best practice and consistency in professional self-regulation in nine bodies:

- General Medical Council
- General Dental Council
- General Optical Council
- General Osteopathic Council
- General Chiropractic Council
- Health Professions Council
- Nursing and Midwifery Council
- Royal Pharmaceutical Society of Great Britain
- Pharmaceutical Society of Northern Ireland.

CHRE's council is its governing body and consists of nine members: seven non-executives and two executives. With parliamentary approval, CHRE can force a regulator to change its rules. It also has the power to refer unduly lenient decisions about professionals' fitness to practise to the High Court for review.

**www.chre.org.uk**

At the same time the Government published its response to the final report of the Shipman Inquiry. Key changes include:

- measures to ensure patients registering concerns are taken seriously
- more systematic use of information about the clinical outcomes of individual practitioners and teams
- bringing together information from different sources for a fuller picture about professionals
- all primary care organisations to adopt best practice in investigating and acting on concerns.

### Further information

*Fifth report – safeguarding patients: lessons from the past – proposals for the future,* Shipman Inquiry, December 2004.

*Good doctors, safer patients: proposals to strengthen the system to assure and improve the performance of doctors and to protect the safety of patients – a report by the chief medical officer,* DH, July 2006.

*Trust, assurance and safety: the regulation of health professionals in the 21st century,* DH, February 2007.

*Learning from tragedy, keeping patients safe: overview of the Government's action programme in response to the recommendations of the Shipman Inquiry*, DH, February 2007.
*Briefing 31: The white paper on the future of professional regulation and the Government's response to the Shipman and other inquiries: what they will mean for employers in the NHS*, NHS Employers, April 2007.

### Continuing professional development

In *A first class service* (see page 126), the DH defined continuing professional development (CPD) as:

> a process of lifelong learning for all individuals and teams which meets the needs of patients and delivers the health outcomes and healthcare priorities of the NHS, and which enables professionals to expand and fulfil their potential.

In a climate of constant change, it is important that members of all professions demonstrate that they are keeping their knowledge and skills up to date: it is no longer sufficient simply to establish competence at the beginning of a career. Many professions, not just in healthcare, have adopted mandatory CPD. For individuals, CPD should:

- maintain professional competence and enable them, their teams and organisation to meet patients' needs, carry out their work with confidence and assist them in the event of an untoward incident
- provide them with the professional and personal satisfaction that they are working to the best of their ability and for the greater benefit of patients, colleagues and their employer
- help sustain motivation and interest in their work
- help meet career aspirations and learning needs, support flexible career pathways and allow them to take on wider responsibilities if necessary
- help them keep their jobs or enhance the possibility of finding another job
- help them identify the skills and knowledge they need to develop, preparing them for future opportunities.

CPD is as important for NHS organisations as it is for individuals. A professional's failure to keep up to date could have serious results, while allowing their skills and knowledge to become obsolete is to waste the investment in their education and training. In *Continuing professional development – quality in the new NHS* (July 1999) the DH stated that 'every health organisation needs to develop a locally managed, systematic approach to CPD'. The core principles are that CPD should be:

- purposeful and patient-centred
- participative, fully involving the individual and other relevant stakeholders

- targeted at identified educational need
- educationally effective
- part of a wider organisational development plan supporting local and national service objectives
- focused on the development needs of clinical teams across traditional professional and service boundaries
- designed to build on previous knowledge, skills and experience
- designed to enhance the skills of interpreting and applying knowledge based on research and development.

**CPD is a cyclical process involving four components**

**Assessment**
of individual and organisational needs

**Planning**
personal development plan requirements

**Implementation**

**Evaluation**
of effectiveness of CPD intervention, and of benefit to patient care

Source: Department of Health

## Code of conduct for NHS managers

Just as doctors, nurses and other health workers have codified ethics, so since 2002 have NHS managers. Written by senior managers in collaboration with the DH, the code states that all NHS managers must:
- make the care and safety of patients their first concern and act to protect them from risk
- respect the public, patients, relatives, carers, NHS staff and partners in other agencies
- be honest and act with integrity
- accept responsibility for their own work and the proper performance of the people they manage

- show their commitment to working as a team member by working with all their colleagues in the NHS and the wider community
- take responsibility for their own learning and development.

NHS organisations must incorporate the code in the contracts of chief executives and directors, and investigate alleged breaches. Those who break the code can be dismissed from the NHS and barred from re-employment within it. The Next Stage Review proposed enhancing the code because managers will be under greater scrutiny as more responsibility is devolved to local level.

### Further information
*Code of conduct for NHS managers*, DH, October 2002.
*Briefing 78: Managing for excellence in the NHS and the code of conduct for NHS managers*, NHS Confederation, February 2003.
www.nhsemployers.org/managementstandards

# 07 Financing the NHS

While the NHS has embraced diversity in the provision of its services, its funding continues to draw overwhelmingly on a single source – taxation – although it does raise a certain amount from charges. However, the way money flows through the system has been drastically reformed with the introduction of 'payment by results'. NHS funding increases ran at record levels for five years until 2008/09; as planned, spending growth from now on will be much slower. The NHS will therefore need to secure the maximum gains from improved efficiency and productivity if it is to continue to meet rising demand for its services.

## Sources of funding

### Taxation

Funding healthcare through taxation ensures universal access to services irrespective of ability to pay. About three-quarters of NHS funding in England came from general taxation – the Consolidated Fund – and just under a fifth from the NHS element of national insurance.

The health service is the second biggest single item of public expenditure (after social security payments), and absorbs 18 per cent of money raised through tax and national insurance contributions (NICs).

General taxation is generally regarded as being a highly efficient way of financing healthcare: it means the Government has both a strong incentive and the capacity to control costs; administrative costs especially tend to be low. As taxation draws revenue from a wide base, it helps minimise distortions in particular sectors of the economy. The social insurance element of NHS financing in the form of NICs paid by employees and employers, although relatively small, has been found to be highly progressive – that is, what people pay directly reflects what they can afford.

However, financing healthcare through taxation means the overall level of resources is constrained by what the Government judges the economy can afford and what is electorally viable, while choices between what services are and are not provided are made centrally. Many would argue that in the past the UK system has gone too far in controlling expenditure, leading to under-investment in the NHS compared with other countries over many years. The degree of individual choice available to patients has tended to be relatively limited, although current policy is trying to address this.

## Charges

The NHS currently charges for a limited number of clinical services – mainly prescriptions, dental treatments, sight tests, glasses and contact lenses. These out-of-pocket payments account for about 2 per cent of NHS funding. The principle remains that they should be paid only by those who can afford them, so those who cannot are not discouraged from seeking advice and treatment. A wide range of exemptions applies, including in most cases young and elderly people and those who are unemployed or on low incomes. The availability of exemptions for clinical reasons is widely seen as illogical and is under review.

### Further information

*Third report of session 2005–06: NHS charges*, House of Commons health committee, July 2006.

## Prescriptions, dental treatment, sight tests

Since April 2009, prescription charges in England have been £7.20 per item. NHS Wales abolished prescription charges in 2007. Scotland reduced them to £5 in 2008 and intends to abolish them by 2011. Prescription charges in Northern Ireland were cut to £3 in 2009 and will be abolished in 2010. Complete abolition has been ruled out in England as it would reduce NHS revenue by about £430 million, but charges for cancer patients were ended in April 2009 and it is planned to do the same for patients with long-term conditions. It is estimated that about 50 per cent of the population of England does not have to pay prescription charges. About 89 per cent of prescription items are dispensed free to patients.

Most courses of dental treatment cost £16.50 or £45.60, depending on their complexity. The maximum charge for complex dental treatment is £198. A sight test costs £19.80, although they have been free in Scotland since 2006.

## Recovering the costs of personal injury

Since the 1930s hospitals have been entitled by law to collect money for treating road traffic accident victims from drivers' insurance companies. Since 2007 the NHS has been able to recover costs from insurance companies for treating patients in all cases where personal injury compensation is paid. In the first eight months of 2008/09, the injury costs recovery scheme raised £87.6 million in England, Scotland and Wales. The Compensation Recovery Unit, part of the Department for Work and

Pensions, collects the charges on the DH's behalf. They are:
- use of an NHS ambulance: £171
- flat rate for treatment without admission: £566
- daily rate for treatment with admission: £695
- maximum in any one case: £41,545.

**Further information**
*Injury costs recovery scheme*, DH, January 2007.
Compensation Recovery Unit **www.dwp.gov.uk/cru**

## Overseas visitors
Anyone who is lawfully 'ordinarily resident' in the UK is entitled to free
NHS treatment in England, regardless of nationality. British citizens who
do not normally live in the UK may have to pay charges for NHS treatment,
regardless of whether they have paid UK taxes and national insurance
contributions, unless they are eligible for certain exemptions. British state
pensioners who split their time between the UK and another European
Economic Area member state are exempt from charges. Responsibility for
deciding who is entitled to free treatment rests with the hospital providing
the treatment. Asylum seekers whose application for refuge in the UK is
outstanding are entitled to use NHS services without charge. In any case,
treatment in an A&E department or walk-in centre, family planning
services, compulsory psychiatric treatment and treatment for certain
communicable diseases are free to all.

## Other sources
Other sources of NHS funding come from land sales and income
generation schemes. For example, income from hospital car-parking fees
has risen from £59.5 million in 2001/02 to more than £100 million.
In addition, the Big Lottery Fund has provided funding for health (as well
as education and the environment). UK-wide it distributed £300 million
to help set up healthy living centres, and gave over £360 million for
coronary heart disease, stroke and cancer services. It also allocated
£84 million for palliative care and support and information services for
people with cancer and other life-threatening conditions.

In addition, there are currently limited charges for non-clinical services
such as single maternity rooms and car parking. (NHSScotland abolished
hospital car-parking charges at the beginning of 2009, and in Northern
Ireland car-parking charges have been abolished for seriously ill patients
and their families.)

## Resource allocation

The Treasury is responsible for overall public expenditure. Every two years it conducts a spending review of all government departments covering three years. After each review, the Department of Health – like all government departments – draws up a public service agreement with the Treasury, setting out what it is expected to provide with its new resources over a three-year period. The DH in turn issues priorities and planning guidance to the NHS in the annual operating framework. The Treasury makes block grants to the Scottish Parliament, Welsh Assembly and the Northern Ireland Assembly, from which they allocate funds for the NHS.

Spending on the NHS divides into these main sectors:
- *hospital and community health services and discretionary family health services* (HCFHS). This covers hospital and community health services, prescribing costs for drugs and appliances and discretionary general medical services (which include reimbursements of GMS GPs' practice staff, premises, out-of-hours and IT expenses). It also includes other centrally funded initiatives, services and special allocations managed centrally by the DH (such as education and training, and research and development).
- *non-discretionary family health services* (FHS). This covers demand-led family health services, including the remuneration of GPs for items such as capitation payments, health promotion and basic practice allowance, the cost of general dental and ophthalmic services, dispensing remuneration and income from dental and prescription charges.
- *central health and miscellaneous services* (CHMS), for example, certain public health functions and support to the voluntary sector.

### Role of PCTs

Since 2003/04 the DH has made 'unified allocations' covering a three-year period direct to primary care trusts. PCTs now control 82 per cent of the NHS budget, and have to plan the use of their resources over the three years as agreed with their strategic health authority. However, they must manage within their annual resource limit total for each year, although they can carry forward planned underspends of up to 0.25 per cent.

These unified budget allocations cover:

- commissioning hospital, mental health and learning disability services
- PCT running costs
- GP and community nurses' prescribing costs
- primary care infrastructure.

Provided they are achieving the targets in their local delivery plan and keep sufficient in reserve to pay GPs, PCTs can use their resources as they see fit.

PCTs are responsible for funding the healthcare of all patients registered with GPs in their area. Under practice-based commissioning, PCTs delegate budgets to GP practices to commission acute, community and emergency care. PCTs' and practices' agreements with providers – NHS trusts, foundation trusts and, increasingly, independent providers – may no longer set activity levels, which are now decided by patient choice and funded through payment by results (see opposite). However, all contracts and agreements do contain planned activity levels profiled across the year.

NHS trusts derive most of their income by providing services in this way, although they also earn some by providing private healthcare and are funded separately for training health professionals. They may also generate some income from shops or car parks on hospital premises.

All providers of NHS services have to publish their costs for individual procedures on a consistent basis in the national schedule of reference costs. This gives details of the unit costs for a range of procedures and treatments, from x-rays to lung transplant surgery and from a visit by a district nurse to a home delivery by a midwife. Commissioners can use the information when negotiating agreements, and identify areas for improving efficiency.

### Deciding allocations

Four factors are taken into account in allocating resources to PCTs:

- weighted capitation targets – set according to a national formula, which calculates a PCT's target share of resources based on its population and their health needs due to deprivation or high mortality and morbidity levels, as well as a 'market forces factor' to account for unavoidable geographical variations in the cost of providing services; the intention is that every PCT should be able to commission similar levels of health services for populations in similar need

**Payment by results**

In a far-reaching change to the way money flows through the NHS in England between commissioners and providers, a system of payment by results has been gradually introduced. The aim is to ensure funding follows the patient, to underpin Government policy on increasing patient choice and encouraging a diversity of providers.

The Government's intention is to provide a transparent system for paying trusts which encourages activity and so helps keep waiting times short. PCTs commission the volume of activity they require for their populations, but instead of drawing up block agreements with NHS trusts as previously, the trusts and other providers are paid for the activity they undertake. A tariff derived from national reference costs removes prices from local negotiation, so that commissioners focus instead on gains in patient choice, quality, shorter waiting time, volumes of activity and efficiency.

Payment by results began in a limited way in 2003/04, and has been gradually extended. By 2008/09 it covered £25 billion worth of activity. Changes to the tariff in 2009/10 are designed to enable pricing to support services independent of their setting and to be more sensitive to the complexity of treatment.

The Next Stage Review recommended providers' income be linked to quality. As a result, under the new Commissioning for Quality and Innovation (CQUIN) payment framework, part of a provider's income will depend on quality improvement. Up to 0.5 per cent of the contract value may be earmarked in this way, a proportion that will increase in subsequent years.

A code of conduct for payment by results sets out core principles, ground rules for organisational behaviour and expectations of how the system should operate – and is intended to minimise disputes.

The Audit Commission concluded that payment by results has been successfully implemented across the NHS and helped hospitals to become more business-like, but so far had had a smaller than expected impact on efficiency and productivity.

**Further information**
*The right result? Payment by results 2003–07*, Audit Commission, February 2008.
*Code of conduct for payment by results*, DH, February 2009.

- recurrent baselines – representing the actual allocation a PCT received in the last allocation round, plus any recurrent adjustments
- distance from target – the difference between target and recurrent baseline
- pace-of-change policy – decided by ministers for each allocation round, this determines the level of increase all PCTs get and the extra for under-target PCTs to move them closer to their weighted capitation targets.

The DH's Advisory Committee on Resource Allocation (ACRA) revised the weighted capitation formula in 2008 to better target funds at places with the worst health outcomes, improve assessment of need and include a new market forces factor to reduce variation between neighbouring PCTs and hospitals. ACRA recommended use of a separate formula to take account of health inequalities; ministers decided to apply this formula to 15 per cent of allocations for 2009/10 and 2010/11.

In 2009/10 the average allocation growth for PCTs is 5.5 per cent, with minimum growth of 5.2 per cent. Planned growth for 2010/11 is also 5.5 per cent, with minimum growth of 5.1 per cent.

### Further information
*Resource allocation: weighted capitation formula – sixth edition*, DH, December 2008.
*Report of the Advisory Committee on Resource Allocation*, DH, December 2008.

## Capital
Capital investment is expenditure – typically on buildings or large items of equipment – that will continue to provide benefits into the future. To count as NHS capital, spending must generally be on assets that individually cost £5,000 or more and are recorded on the balance sheet as fixed assets.

The NHS's main sources of capital are Government funds, receipts from land sales and the private finance initiative.

### Allocating capital
The DH allocates operational capital to PCTs according to a national needs-based formula. They can spend it as they choose, but it is mainly used for maintaining buildings and replacing equipment.

Strategic capital is allocated to SHAs according to a weighted capitation formula to fund schemes they decide are priorities for bringing about major change.

## Vital statistics: NHS capital 2008/09 (£m)

1  Government spending: 3,643
2  Receipts from land sales: 286
3  PFI investment: 1,422
4  Foundation trusts: 924
   **Total: 6,275**

Source: Department of Health

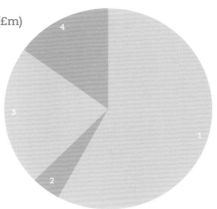

Foundation trusts do not rely on allocations of operational or strategic capital but are free to reinvest all cash generated from their activities to maintain and replace their assets. They may also borrow capital, from commercial banks or the DH, under 'prudential borrowing' arrangements if their projections of future cash flows show they would be able to afford to pay back the sum with interest. Monitor assigns each foundation trust a 'prudential borrowing limit', fixing the amount of debt it may take on.

Since 2007 NHS trusts may also borrow capital under a similar regime to that for foundation trusts, but approved by SHAs and the DH: access to capital funding is decided by the affordability of proposed investments and financed by loans and borrowing subject to a prudential borrowing regime. However, NHS trusts' first source of capital financing is internally generated cash. Since 2008, PCTs have also been free to set their own local investment plans subject to agreement with their SHA. In 2009/10, £500 million is available for this.

Capital to fund some specific policy initiatives is still allocated centrally. These 'programme budgets' include:
• community hospital development
• fluoridation
• substance misuse
• learning disability service reprovision
• mental health facilities
• energy efficiency.

Capital funding (excluding PFI) for 2009/10 is planned to increase to £5.6 billion and to £6.3 billion in 2010/11.

## Private finance initiative (PFI)

PFI involves a public–private partnership between an NHS organisation and a private sector consortium that makes private capital available for health service projects. All major NHS capital projects are expected to consider whether PFI could represent a value-for-money solution.

The private sector consortium will usually include a construction company, a funding organisation and a facilities management provider. Contracts for major PFI schemes may be for 30 years or more and are typically DBFO (design, build, finance and operate) projects. This means the private sector partner is responsible for:

- designing the facilities (based on the requirements specified by the NHS)
- building the facilities (to time and at a fixed cost)
- financing the capital cost (with the return to be recovered through continuing to make the facilities available and meeting NHS requirements)
- operating the facilities (providing facilities management and other support services).

PFI schemes must demonstrate value for money, which is usually achieved by the PFI partner assuming risks which would otherwise have been borne by the public sector, and by efficiency savings. The PFI contract sets out the performance standards required of the consortium. The NHS makes no payments until services are provided to the agreed standard, and then they must be maintained to ensure full payment.

The aims of PFI are to increase innovation and reduce the overall risks associated with procuring new assets and services for the NHS, as well as to improve the quality and cost-effectiveness of public services. Because the PFI partner's capital is at risk, they have an incentive to perform well throughout the life of the contract, while private sector management, commercial and creative skills are harnessed for the NHS's benefit.

Critics have questioned whether PFI will really provide long-term value for money for the NHS, and have claimed services have been cut in some cases to make schemes affordable. The National Audit Office found that when PFI contracts had to be altered due to new policy initiatives or changing local circumstances, the changes often did not offer value for money.

The Government has said: 'PFI is only a procurement tool – not an end in itself – and will only be used in cases where it offers value for money to the taxpayer and the NHS.' It is not advised in projects involving rapid change, such as IT. As the NHS is undergoing a period of rapid change, it can be argued that PFI will need to adapt to accommodate the changes.

The launch of the Treasury report, *PFI: strengthening long-term partnerships*, confirmed the Government's commitment to a PFI investment programme for public services and describes the steps it is taking to strengthen PFI with measures to increase flexibility and reinforce the requirement for value for money.

However, the banking crisis has made the future of PFI uncertain as banks' current reluctance to lend money means they are unwilling to finance PFI schemes. Nevertheless, the Prime Minister has pledged that 'all health service investment we want to see happen has been budgeted for and will go forward'.

Of 93 major hospitals schemes between 1997 and mid-2008, 70 were built using PFI and 23 were funded through public capital. Another 34 hospitals were under construction.

### Further information
*PFI: strengthening long-term partnerships*, HM Treasury, March 2006
*Rebuilding the NHS: a new generation of healthcare facilities*, DH, June 2007.
*Making changes in operational PFI projects, National Audit Office*, January 2008.

## NHS Local Improvement Finance Trust (LIFT)
NHS LIFT aims to encourage investment in primary care and community-based facilities and services to achieve the NHS Plan target of 500 one-stop primary care centres and the refurbishment or replacement of up to 3,000 GP premises. It is similar to PFI, except that it is a joint venture between PCTs, the private sector partner, local authorities and GPs.

Community Health Partnerships (formerly Partnerships for Health), a public–private partnership between the DH and Partnerships UK, was set up to invest money in NHS LIFT and help attract additional private funding; the DH became the sole owner in 2006. At local level, NHS LIFT is not a single trust but a series of local public–private partnerships between PCTs, the private sector, CHP and local authorities. The resulting partnership is a LIFT company, which is a local joint venture.

By early 2008, there had been 162 new GP premises had been built under the LIFT programme, with a further 50 under construction. NHS LIFT seeks investment in primary care developments by bundling them together. So far, 48 local LIFT schemes are renting accommodation to GPs, pharmacists, opticians, dentists and others on a lease basis. The latest wave of schemes adds the option to include clinical and facilities management services as well as buildings and maintenance. The total value of the LIFT programme is £1.5 billion.

In the 2008 pre-Budget report, the Government announced it would allow PCTs to extend LIFT schemes to enable them to manage PCTs' entire estates.

### Further information
*Innovation in the NHS: local improvement finance trusts*, National Audit Office, May 2005.
www.communityhealthpartnerships.co.uk

## NHS spending

### The era of growth
From the time the NHS was founded until the end of the 1990s, its annual average increase in funding was just over 3 per cent – slightly more than the real growth in the economy as a whole. However, from the early 1980s, real spending changes were erratic. Taking into account the level of inflation in the NHS rather than in the general economy, annual average growth was about 0.9 per cent from 1983 to 1987, rising to 2 per cent from 1987 to 1992 and 1.4 per cent from 1992 to 1997. In 2000 the Government announced its intention to raise the share of national income spent on health to the European average: it then ranked 14th out of the 15 EU countries.

In 2001 Derek Wanless was commissioned to produce the first evidence-based assessment of the NHS's long-term resource requirements. He produced a similar report for NHS Wales in 2003 (see page 258), while in Northern Ireland the Appleby Report of 2005 (see page 271) sought to predict future needs and resources.

As a result of Wanless's report on the English NHS, the 2002 Budget heralded major increases in net spending until 2007/08: from £53.7 billion to £85.6 billion in England alone. These were the largest sustained increases in any five-year period in NHS history: an annual average increase of 7.4 per cent in real terms between 2002/03 and 2007/08, a total increase of 43 per cent in real terms over the period. This translates into a

## Vital statistics: UK health spending as a percentage of GDP

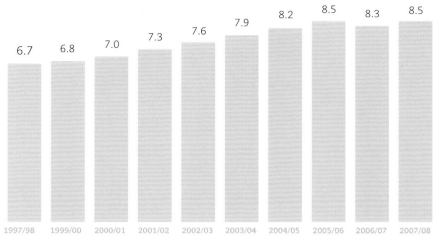

| 1997/98 | 1999/00 | 2000/01 | 2001/02 | 2002/03 | 2003/04 | 2004/05 | 2005/06 | 2006/07 | 2007/08 |
| 6.7 | 6.8 | 7.0 | 7.3 | 7.6 | 7.9 | 8.2 | 8.5 | 8.3 | 8.5 |

Source: HM Treasury

rise in NHS spending per head from £890 in 2001/02 to £1,676 in 2007/08. The aim was to put the health service on a 'sound long-term financial footing', making significant investment in IT, buildings and equipment, and raising NHS spending to the EU average. To help pay for these increases, national insurance contributions were raised by 1 per cent from April 2003.

**The era of recession**

NHS spending has long been planned to increase at the slower rate of 4 per cent a year in real terms for three years from 2008/09. This will take the total budget to £110 billion by 2010/11. However, the global economic downturn has brought added pressure on public finances and sharpened the need to improve value for money through greater efficiency. This harsher economic climate coincides with new challenges for the health service arising from the Next Stage Review.

The NHS is in a strong position to weather the immediate downturn: it made a £1.67 billion surplus in 2007/08, much more than the £900 million combined surplus and contingency that had been planned in case of sudden financial pressures or new policy priorities. The contingency was not needed and the surplus grew as NHS organisations exceeded savings plans and the price of generic medicines fell.

**Key text: Wanless Report**

In 2001 the then Chancellor commissioned Derek Wanless, former chief executive of NatWest Bank, to examine demand and cost pressures in the NHS over the next 20 years and recommend the spending needed for a 'publicly funded, comprehensive, high-quality service available on the basis of clinical need and not ability to pay'. His report was published in April 2002.

Wanless found that although an ageing population would be an important influence, this would not be the main factor driving up costs. Improving information and communication technology would be key to achieving more choice and higher quality services, while the NHS would have to change its skill-mix and ways of working, and enhance the role of primary care.

Wanless concluded that spending would need to rise between 9.4 per cent and 11.3 per cent of GDP by 2021, with the fastest growth before 2008. He warned: 'Both additional resources and radical reform are vital: neither would succeed without the other.'

Wanless's figures assume that plans for huge expansion of the workforce are achieved, that IT spend can be doubled and used productively while the NHS fulfils commitments on waiting times and national service frameworks. If productivity improvement falls short of 2 per cent a year, spending will need to rise to an even higher proportion of GDP.

Reviewing progress after five years, Wanless noted significant improvements in staffing, equipment, infrastructure, waiting times and care for coronary heart disease, cancer, stroke and mental health. But he was disappointed that increased funding had not resulted in the increased productivity envisaged. In particular, he was alarmed at delays to the IT programme and at the dramatic rise in obesity. He criticised the introduction of policies and structural changes without adequate preparation, and concluded the NHS was no longer on course to achieve a 'world-class' service by 2021. On his projections the NHS could be short of funding by between £7.2 billion and £15.2 billion by 2010. Nevertheless, he said: 'Despite these concerns we conclude that the broad direction of Government health policy is the right one.'

**Further Information**

*Securing our future: taking a long-term view. Final report*, HM Treasury, April 2002.
*Our future health secured? A review of NHS funding and performance*, King's Fund, September 2007.

However, the NHS will be allowed to use only £800 million of its surplus during the next two years. It has to find 'very substantial' efficiency savings in 2010/11 – possibly as much as £1.5 billion – while an increase in employers' national insurance contributions from 2011 will add significantly to the wage bill. When the period covered by the current comprehensive spending review ends in 2011, the NHS is likely to face a prolonged phase of very low growth, probably in line with other public spending – 1.3 per cent in 2011/12, falling to 1.1 per cent in 2013/14. It may therefore need to devise some radical approaches to efficiency savings in the coming years.

**Further information**
*Pre-Budget report – facing global challenges: supporting people through difficult times*, HM Treasury, November 2008.

## Has the NHS given value for money?
Clinical outcomes, waiting times and patient satisfaction have all improved, while many other productivity gains are still working their way through the system. The true picture can be clouded by measures that often do not accurately reflect what the NHS does and confuse quality improvements with a loss of productivity. However, examining the NHS UK-wide, the Office for National Statistics claimed that while output was 50 per cent higher in 2006 than 1995, the volume of resources going in was 67 per cent higher, meaning productivity has fallen.

Despite unprecedented funding levels, the NHS in England overspent by £216 million in 2004/05 and by £547 million in 2005/06. These financial problems had no single underlying cause, with little correlation between the size of an organisation's deficit and its allocation per head, nor with its performance rating.

Since then, finances have improved markedly, with the NHS achieving surpluses in 2006/07 and 2007/08. But despite the £510 million surplus in 2006/07, the House of Commons public accounts committee noted more than one in five NHS organisations were still in deficit, with striking regional variations in financial performance. It concluded the return to overall financial balance resulted from the DH's tighter management of NHS financial flows and a support programme for organisations in difficulty.

After the NHS made a £1.67 billion surplus in 2007/08, the Audit Commission found 'an overall picture of financial improvement for many

NHS organisations', with 93 per cent of NHS trusts and PCTs meeting or exceeding minimum standards for their use of financial resources. In addition, the National Audit Office found only 3 per cent of NHS organisations reporting a deficit – down from 22 per in 2006/07 – despite a 5 per cent increase in non-emergency hospital procedures and a 2 per cent increase in GP consultations, with staffing levels remaining stable. It recorded that the quality of financial management had improved during the year.

### Further information

*Explaining NHS deficits 2003/04-2005/06: chief economist's report on NHS deficits*, DH, February 2007.
*Review of the NHS financial year 2006/07*, Audit Commission, October 2007.
*Public service productivity: health care*, ONS, January 2008.
*Report on the NHS summarised accounts 2006/07: achieving financial balance*, House of Commons public accounts committee, June 2008.
*Auditors' local evaluation 2007/08: summary results for NHS trusts and PCTs*, Audit Commission, October 2008.
*Financial management in the NHS: report on the NHS summarised accounts 2007/08*, National Audit Office/Audit Commission, December 2008.

## Where the money is spent

In England, NHS total expenditure (revenue and capital), including money available from charges and receipts, was expected to be over £102.3 billion in 2008/09. The largest part of NHS spending is on hospital and community health services, discretionary family health services and related services. For 2008/09, total planned revenue expenditure for hospital, community and family health services is £94.2 billion and total planned capital expenditure is £4.8 billion.

The domination of spending on acute services reflects the demand for emergency treatment and the continuing emphasis on reducing waiting lists and waiting times. Healthcare for people over 65 accounts for more than 40 per cent of the total expenditure.

## Efficiency savings

Efficiency and productivity vary across the NHS, and the Government argues that significant benefits could come from trusts following best practice. Efficiency programmes must be underpinned by 'best value' principles that recognise the importance of quality improvement as well as cost reduction.

Vital statistics: How hospital and community health service (HCHS) spending is divided

1  Acute: 59%
2  Mental health: 14%
3  Community health services: 12%
4  Accident and emergency: 4%
5  Learning disability: 4%
6  Other: 4%
7  Maternity: 3%

Source: Department of Health

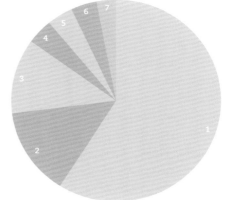

Spending increases usually come with caveats about the level of efficiency savings the NHS is expected to make. As a result of the comprehensive spending review it is expected to make efficiency gains of 3 per cent in each of the three years to 2010/11. However, the DH announced in the operating framework for 2009/10: 'in the current economic climate, it is appropriate that the NHS with the other public services goes further and deeper in making efficiencies to contribute to returning the economy to balance'.

The NHS is therefore expected to explore opportunities identified in the cross-government operational efficiency programme, which include:
• using shared services for back-office operations
• more use of collaborative procurement
• more commercial and efficient use of property
• more encouragement for frontline innovation.

However, such top-down modelling exercises often make assumptions that bear little resemblance to what is possible locally.

**Measuring inflation**
Increases in the cost of goods and services used by the NHS are measured by the health service cost index (HSCI). This weights together price increases for a broad range of items – for example: drugs, medical equipment, fuel and telephone charges. Pay inflation must also be taken into account to calculate the rate of inflation affecting the hospital and community health services.

Vital statistics: HCHS inflation (%)

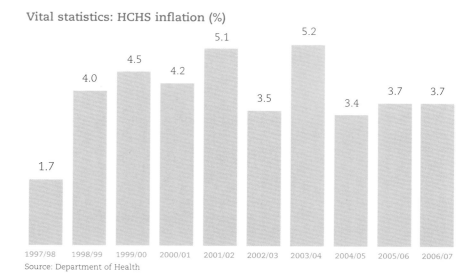

Source: Department of Health

## Buying goods and services

### Pharmaceutical Price Regulation Scheme

The PPRS regulates the prices of branded medicines and the profits that manufacturers are allowed to make on their sales to the NHS. It is a voluntary agreement made between the DH and the Association of the British Pharmaceutical Industry. A series of voluntary agreements has limited branded medicine prices and profits since 1957, each lasting five years or so.

Agreements cover all licensed, branded prescription medicines sold to the NHS. They do not cover products without a brand name (generics) nor over-the-counter branded products except when prescribed by a doctor. The PPRS is a UK-wide scheme, and covers around 80 per cent by value of the medicines used in the NHS in both primary and secondary care. The total NHS drugs bill in England is £10.5 billion a year, including both branded and generic medicines and drugs prescribed in the community as well as in hospital. Net expenditure on medicines in the community is over £7 billion.

The PPRS seeks to achieve reasonable prices for the NHS, while recognising that the industry needs to earn the money to enable it to develop and market new and improved medicines. The latest agreement has secured for the NHS a 3.9 per cent price reduction for branded prescription medicines from February 2009 and a further 1.9 per cent cut from January 2010. Subject to discussion, the DH will introduce generic substitution in January 2010, and further price adjustments each January will take account of savings from this. The DH hopes these more flexible pricing arrangements will enable companies to supply drugs to the NHS at lower initial prices, with the option of higher prices if value is proven at a later date. The Government has promised measures to allow patients faster access to clinically proven new drugs.

A maximum price scheme for generics – on which the NHS spends over £2 billion a year – was introduced in 2000 to restrain the drugs bill after steep price rises, saving around £330 million a year. Since 2004, where there is a limited number of manufacturers of a generic medicine or the supply is concentrated, manufacturers have to seek the DH's agreement to any price increase. Manufacturers and wholesalers must submit quarterly information on income revenues, cost of purchases and volumes of transactions.

### Further information
*PPRS market study report*, OFT, February 2007.
*The Pharmaceutical Price Regulation Scheme*, ABPI/DH, August 2008.

## NHS Shared Business Services

Launched as a joint venture between the DH and a private sector company in 2005, the intention is that SBS provides high-quality, cost-effective business services such as processing financial transactions, so that frontline organisations can concentrate on patient care. It currently provides finance, accounting and payroll services to over 100 NHS organisations. With 1,000 employees at six locations in the UK and India, it processes 300,000 invoices each month and 100,000 payslips for NHS staff.
www.sbs.nhs.uk

## NHS Purchasing and Supply Agency

This agency is responsible for ensuring the NHS gets the best value for money when purchasing other goods and services. It is not a trading organisation but advises on policy and the strategic direction of procurement across the NHS. Part of PASA has been merged with NHS Logistics to create NHS Supply Chain, which specialises in the supply and delivery of healthcare-related products and is managed by a private company. The rest of PASA's organisational structure is currently under review.
www.pasa.nhs.uk
www.supplychain.nhs.uk

## NHS Business Services Authority

This special health authority was set up in April 2006 to be the main processing facility for payment, reimbursement, remuneration and reconciliation for NHS patients, employees and others. It was formed from the Dental Practice Board, NHS Pensions Agency and the Prescription Pricing Authority.
www.nhsbsa.nhs.uk

## NHS Counter Fraud Service

The NHS Counter Fraud Service was established to tackle fraud and corruption throughout the NHS, whether involving professionals, staff, patients or contractors. The service has more than 300 trained and accredited counter-fraud specialists throughout the NHS in England and Wales. Since 1999 it is estimated to have recovered £60 million. Fraud by NHS professionals has fallen by up to 60 per cent and fraud by patients by 55 per cent since 1998. The NHS fraud and corruption reporting line is 0800 028 4060.
www.nhsbsa.nhs.uk/CounterFraud

# 08 Staffing and human resources

As the UK's largest employer – indeed, one of the largest employers in the world – the NHS attaches special importance to good human resources policy and practice. Staff costs account for about 75 per cent of hospital expenditure. Effective recruitment, retention and remuneration of a well-trained and well-motivated workforce are seen as crucial factors in achieving the Government's ambitions for patient care.

Recent years have seen significant investment to expand the NHS workforce and revise contracts to reflect changing patterns of care. Integrating staff between the NHS, the independent healthcare sector and social care is now a key theme. So too is improving staff productivity and efficiency as spending increases diminish. Organisations must also do their utmost to engage staff in designing ways of improving services, and this was reflected in the Next Stage Review, where workforce issues were a central theme. Staff responsibilities are also a major part of the NHS Constitution (see page 115).

## Workforce planning

The Next Stage Review recommended a more employer-based system for workforce planning. Strategic health authorities will co-ordinate overall plans for their area and retain the lead role for education commissioning. Primary care trusts will link workforce planning to health needs, and providers will integrate workforce and service plans locally. These new arrangements are being implemented through a variety of models.

The review also proposed a centre of excellence to support workforce planning by developing capacity and capability and carrying out long-term horizon-scanning. It would be accountable to the DH's director general of workforce, and provide the NHS with access to leading thinkers and an evidence base to shape its workforce strategy. The centre would analyse labour market dynamics and provide NHS organisations with workforce supply and demand analysis and forecasting intelligence.

**Further information**
*A high quality workforce: NHS Next Stage review*, DH, June 2008.
*Briefing 47: NHS Next Stage review: workforce issues*, NHS Employers, July 2008.
*Proposals for a centre of excellence for workforce strategy and planning*, King's Fund, January 2009.
www.ournhs.nhs.uk
www.nhsemployers.org

# NHS staff by main staff groups, 2008

### Professionally qualified clinical staff: 51.2%

1 All doctors: 9.8%

2 Qualified ambulance staff: 1.3%

3 Qualified ST&T staff: 10.4%

4 Qualified nurses, including practice nurses: 29.8%

### Support to clinical staff: 32.7%

5 GP practice staff: 6.8%

6 Support to doctors and nurses: 20.9%

7 Support to ST&T staff: 4%

8 Support to ambulance staff: 1%

### NHS infrastructure support staff: 16%

9 Central functions: 7.7%

10 Hotel, property and estates: 5.4%

11 Manager and senior manager: 2.9%

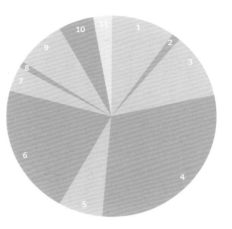

## Staff numbers

The NHS workforce has grown by 22 per cent since 1998, and now stands at 1.3 million in England. Numbers increased steadily between 2000 and 2005 but declined in the following two years. The workforce increased by 2.8% in 2008 as trusts successfully delivered against targets such as 18 weeks. The NHS is now aiming for a 'steady state' in which supply of labour is more closely matched with demand.

### Further information

*Staff in the NHS 1998–2008 (England)*, The Information Centre, 2009.

## Social Partnership Forum

The NHS Social Partnership Forum, set up in 2007, brings together NHS unions, NHS Employers and the DH to discuss current issues and develop joint initiatives to tackle national problems.

The SPF's work currently covers five key areas:
• workforce planning – including maximising opportunities for newly qualified healthcare professionals
• partnership working
• staff security (terms and conditions in a plural system)
• knowledge and skills framework
• staff engagement and the NHS staff survey.

In 2008 the Government announced a £500,000 fund to promote and develop partnership working between employers and trade unions locally and regionally, building on the SPF model.

### Further information

*Partnership agreement: an agreement between DH, NHS Employers and NHS trade unions*, DH/NHS Employers/NHS trade unions, February 2007.

## Key organisation: NHS Employers

NHS Employers represents trusts in England on workforce issues and helps employers to ensure the NHS is a place where people want to work. It reflects employers' views and acts on their behalf in four priority areas:
• pay and negotiations
• recruitment and planning the workforce
• healthy and productive workplaces
• employment policy and practice.

NHS Employers, set up in 2004, is part of the NHS Confederation. The DH sets the broad framework within which it operates, but employers themselves drive the agenda. Its policy board plays an important role in making decisions about the work, position and direction of the organisation, with members drawn from across the NHS.
**www.nhsemployers.org**

## NHS Careers

NHS Careers is a service providing information on careers in the NHS in England. It consists of a 24-hour contact centre, website, literature and supporting services for NHS employers, schools, colleges and careers advisers. Launched in 1999, it aims to raise awareness among the potential future workforce of the 350 careers the NHS offers. It has developed a service for 14–19-year-olds to find out what working in the NHS is like, and another where undergraduates on clinical and non-clinical courses in England can look at their options for a career in the NHS.

www.nhscareers.nhs.uk
www.stepintothenhs.nhs.uk
www.whatcanIdowithmydegree.nhs.uk

## NHS Jobs

NHS Jobs is an online recruitment service offering details of job vacancies throughout the NHS in England and Wales. Launched in 2003, it provides employers with online tools to manage every stage of the recruitment cycle. Each month it carries details of around 20,000 career opportunities in the NHS, attracts 4.5 million visits and receives job applications from more than 250,000 jobseekers. Ninety per cent of NHS job applications are made through the website. Every NHS trust in England and Wales is registered to advertise with NHS Jobs, which is estimated to save the NHS about £1 million a week in advertising and recruitment administration costs.

### Further information

*Briefing 54: NHS Jobs – delivering the future for NHS recruitment*, NHS Employers, November 2008.

www.jobs.nhs.uk

## Training

New ways of working, new treatments and procedures and the shift of services from hospitals to the community all have implications for training the healthcare workforce. During 2009/10 responsibility for medical education is moving entirely to the General Medical Council while the Postgraduate Medical Education and Training Board is abolished. Deaneries oversee the placing of students in their training within hospitals. Medical Education England (see page 194) now also has a role. The Nursing and Midwifery Council sets standards for nurse education.

## Spotlight on policy: Modernising careers

Pre-registration education and training for nurses, midwives and healthcare scientists is changing to reflect their evolving roles – a trend boosted by the Next Stage Review's emphasis on strong clinical leadership. This means greater flexibility and more emphasis on practice during learning, and makes the education system more responsive to the NHS's needs.

Modernising Medical Careers (MMC) introduced a major reform of postgraduate medical education and training from 2005 with new foundation and specialty training programmes. Difficulties experienced with recruitment to specialty training programmes in 2007 prompted an independent review of MMC by Sir John Tooke, which led to further reform to the structure of postgraduate training.

Medical Education England is a strategic advisory body for doctors, dentists, healthcare scientists and pharmacists, recommended by the Next Stage Review and set up in 2009. It is expected to provide a coherent voice on education and training, scrutinising and advising on the quality of workforce planning nationally. Membership is drawn from employers, professional bodies, staff organisations, the DH and other interested organisations.

Under the Modernising Nursing Careers programme, the DH has consulted on a new structure for nurses' careers based on five patient pathways:
- children, family and public health
- first contact, access and urgent care
- supporting long-term care
- acute and critical care
- mental health and psychosocial care.

The Nursing and Midwifery Council conducted a review of pre-registration nursing to ensure all those who qualify as new registrants are fit for practice. As a result, the profession will become all-graduate.

The NHS's 55,000-strong healthcare scientist workforce includes 50 scientific disciplines encompassing biology, genetics, physiology, physics and engineering. As science and technology advance, greater clinical scientific expertise will be required, and healthcare scientists will take on broader roles, including leadership, management and education.

Existing training and career arrangements will therefore need to change. The DH has consulted on clearer pathways into healthcare science careers defined through three stages, with the ability to progress between them subject to entry requirements:
• healthcare science assistant
• healthcare scientist practitioner
• healthcare scientist.

**Further information**
*Aspiring to Excellence – final report of the independent inquiry into modernising medical careers led by Professor Sir John Tooke*, MMC Inquiry, January 2008.
*Towards a framework for post-registration nursing careers: consultation response report*, DH, July 2008.
*The Government response to the health select committee report 'Modernising medical careers'*, TSO, July 2008.
*Briefing 52: Medical training and careers – the employers' vision*, NHS Employers, November 2008.
*The future of the healthcare science workforce. Modernising scientific careers, the next steps: a consultation*, DH, November 2008.
*Implementing the Tooke report: Department of Health update*, DH, November 2008.
**www.mmc.nhs.uk**
**www.nmc-uk.org**

## Productivity

As the NHS will receive spending increases of 4 per cent for the next three years, compared to the 7.4 per cent average increases it has enjoyed for the last five years, it is facing greater pressure than ever to improve workforce productivity. With the economic downturn its productivity improvements are expected to go even 'further and deeper' than they otherwise would.

Trusts are measured on a range of workforce productivity indicators developed by the NHS Institute (see page 196). These cover:
• staff turnover
• absence levels
• use of temporary staff
• finished consultant episodes.

Finished consultant episodes are used as a measure of the amount of work undertaken by medical staff. Data on relative performance on this measure has been collected and sent to the NHS for use in local discussion on improving productivity. These measures are being kept under review.

**Further information**
NHS Institute indicators www.productivity.nhs.uk

**Spotlight on policy: 18-week wait**
The NHS operating framework for 2009/10 states: 'No one should wait more than 18 weeks from the time they are referred to the start of their hospital treatment, unless it is clinically appropriate to do so or they choose to wait longer', a target first set in 2004 to be met by the end of 2008.

Achieving this was one of the major workforce challenges facing the NHS. By September 2008, 105 acute trusts and 96 PCTs had achieved the target, while 90.2 per cent of admitted patients began treatment within 18 weeks of referral; the median waiting time was 8.3 weeks. Of non-admitted patients, 95.7 began treatment within 18 weeks, with a median waiting time of 4.4 weeks. By the end of March 2009 the target had been achieved. www.18weeks.nhs.uk

**Key organisation: NHS Institute for Innovation and Improvement**
The Institute superseded the NHS Modernisation Agency in 2005. A special health authority based at Warwick University, it aims to promote a culture of innovation and lifelong learning for all NHS staff. It supports the rapid adoption and spread of new ideas by providing practical guidance on local, safe implementation. With an annual budget of £80 million, the NHS Institute is particularly interested in service transformation, technology and product innovation, leadership development and learning. www.institute.nhs.uk

# Pay and pensions

The pay and conditions of NHS staff are developed mainly through collective bargaining between NHS Employers and staff organisations, which also represent staff on a wide range of other employment issues. Most staff are members of trade unions or professional associations, and the NHS seeks 'partnership working' on key employment issues. Most NHS staff organisations have a professional and collective bargaining role. NHS Employers negotiates pay, conditions and contracts with the unions, on behalf of employers. GPs are independent self-employed contractors and the contract which sets their income is negotiated by the British Medical Association and NHS Employers.

### Agenda for Change

The Agenda for Change pay system applies to 1.3 million NHS staff across the UK, with the exception of doctors, dentists and the most senior managers. Staff are paid on the basis of the jobs they are doing and the skills and knowledge they apply to these jobs. This is underpinned by a job evaluation scheme specifically designed for the NHS.

The NHS Knowledge and Skills Framework supports personal development and career progression, linked to annual development reviews and personal development plans. It allows staff to progress by taking on new responsibilities.

The job evaluation system and harmonised conditions of service under Agenda for Change should provide a defence against equal pay claims in the future. However, NHS trade unions argue that some of their members can make claims under the Equal Pay Act where assimilation to Agenda for Change has revealed past unequal pay was based on gender difference. They are seeking up to six years' back pay in these cases. In addition, contingency fee lawyers are challenging some transitional elements of the Agenda for Change implementation (including the pay protection arrangements and the national recruitment and retention premiums) on equal pay grounds. One employment tribunal has heard a test case on the national issues concerning equal pay, and a decision is expected in April 2009. This decision may be subject to appeal to the Employment Appeal Tribunal.

NHS Employers, the DH and NHS trade unions agreed a multi-year pay deal for staff on the Agenda for Change pay system for three years from 2008/09. Its main features are:
- all staff to get a pay increase between 7.6 and 7.9 per cent over the three years
- a 5.8 per cent increase in the NHS minimum wage to £6.77 per hour.

### Further information
*From pay reform to system improvement – making the most of Agenda for Change*, NHS Employers, 2006.
*The NHS knowledge and skills framework (KSF): essential guide for NHS staff*, NHS Employers, 2007.
*NHS pay modernisation in England: Agenda for Change*, National Audit Office, January 2009.
www.nhsemployers.org/agendaforchange

### Contract for GPs
A new GP contract for general medical services (GMS) was implemented across the UK in 2004 and revisions to the contract were introduced in 2006 following negotiations between NHS Employers and the British Medical Association's General Practitioners Committee (GPC). The contract aims to reward practices for providing high-quality care, improve GPs' working lives and ensure patients benefit from a wider range of services in the community.

The GMS contract:
- is between the PCT and the practice rather than with each GP. This is intended to give practices greater freedom to design services for local needs while encouraging better teamworking and skill-mix
- helps GPs to manage their workload by enabling practices to transfer some services – including out-of-hours services – to their PCT.

A key component of the GMS contract is the Quality and Outcomes Framework (QOF) which resources and rewards practices for delivering high-quality care (see page 129).

Changes for 2009/10 are intended to distribute resources across practices more fairly, rewarding those that provide new services. QOF payments will increasingly reflect the prevalence of long-term health conditions, to help address health inequalities by ensuring proportionately greater funding for practices in deprived areas.

## Contracts for other doctors and dentists

The current consultants' contract, introduced in 2003, is designed to provide a more effective system of planning and timetabling consultants' duties and activities for the NHS. It gives NHS employers the ability to manage consultants' time in ways that best meet local service needs and priorities. For consultants, it means greater transparency about the commitments expected of them and greater clarity over the support they need from employers to make the maximum effective contribution to improving patient services.

The current contractual arrangements for doctors in hospital and public health training have been in force since December 2000. Junior doctors' hours are required to reduce to levels set in the European working-time directive by August 2009 and the contract facilitates this.

A new contract for staff grade and associate specialist doctors was agreed in 2008. It applies to 13,000 non-consultant career grade NHS doctors and to all new entrants to the new specialty doctor grade. Annual appraisal, job planning and objective setting are essential components of the new contract.

A salaried dentists' contract was implemented in early 2008. A new single pay spine covers dentists, senior dentists, specialist dentists and managerial dentists. The new pay structure is supported by mandatory annual appraisals and job planning to assist career development.

NHS Employers and the Pharmaceutical Services Negotiating Committee are discussing changes to the community pharmacy contract following the Government's white paper, *Pharmacy in England: building on strengths, delivering the future* (see page 77).

### Further information

*Fifty-ninth report of session 2006/07: Pay modernisation – a new contract for NHS consultants in England*, House of Commons public accounts committee, November 2007.
*Briefing 41: Contract proposals for specialty doctors and associate specialists – introduction for employers*, NHS Employers, March 2008.
*Briefing 53: The consultant contract programme*, NHS Employers, November 2008.
www.nhsemployers.org/pay-conditions

### Pensions, retirement and redundancy

Changes to the NHS pension scheme for England and Wales came into effect in April 2008. They aim to ensure the scheme continues to meet the needs of a modern NHS and its staff, and is sustainable in the longer term. Clear processes and procedures for handling absence and supporting staff through rehabilitation, redeployment or ill health retirements are part of this. Employees in the scheme before April 2008 will be able to choose whether to move to the new arrangements, with the transfer process lasting three years from June 2009.
www.nhsemployers.org/pensions

## The NHS as an employer

The NHS recognises staff as its greatest asset and knows that to recruit and retain the right people it needs to practise excellence in employment. This includes treating staff with respect and supporting them in their work; valuing equality and diversity; ensuring a healthy workplace; offering flexible working; and providing training and opportunities for development. The NHS Constitution sets out for the first time what employers can expect from staff and the commitment to staff from NHS employers (see page 115).

### Staff engagement

Staff 'engagement' is a high priority for the NHS as it can improve morale, productivity, organisational performance and patient experience. Research indicates that staff satisfaction – and retention, discretionary effort and productivity – are closely associated with how staff feel about their employer and their sense of engagement with their workplace.

The results of the sixth national NHS staff survey were published by the Healthcare Commission in 2009. The survey, in which 160,000 staff in 390 trusts took part, found staff were generally satisfied in their jobs, that 90 per cent felt their role ultimately made a difference to patients and that 95 per cent had taken part in some training. But 12 per cent had experienced physical violence, and only 31 per cent thought their trust valued their work. Better engagement is therefore crucial to ensuring the NHS can recruit and retain staff in a competitive market.

Engagement is achieved when employees have a positive attitude towards the organisation and its values. DH research on what matters to NHS staff identified four themes:
- resources to deliver quality care
- support to do a good job
- a worthwhile job with a chance to develop
- the opportunity to improve the way staff work.

The DH set up a national policy group on staff engagement in 2008, which will commission research on how managers can have a positive impact on the employee experience.

**Further information**
*NHS national staff survey 2007*, Healthcare Commission, April 2008.
*What matters to staff in the NHS*, Ipsos MORI/DH, June 2008.
*Briefing 50: Staff engagement in the NHS*, NHS Employers, November 2008.

## Equality and diversity
The NHS aims to incorporate equality and diversity into all its workforce strategies and to highlight how it can contribute to improved health and better access to health services. NHS Employers helps trusts to embed equality and diversity in their organisations so they are able to build, manage and retain a diverse workforce, reflecting the communities they serve. Key areas include guidance on meeting employers' legal and statutory responsibilities on equality and diversity and advice on diversity monitoring to help organisations benchmark and track progress. It helps organisations enhance their leadership and ability to make progress on the equality and diversity agenda, as well as providing practical tools on key areas such as developing single equality schemes.

**Further information**
*Briefing 48: Single equality schemes in the NHS: the developing picture*, NHS Employers, November 2008.
*Briefing 49: Equality impact assessments in the NHS – a guide for employers*, NHS Employers, January 2009.
*Briefing 58: Monitoring for diversity: what healthcare employers need to know and do*, NHS Employers, January 2009.

## Stress and bullying

Stress is estimated to cause 30 per cent of sickness absence and cost the NHS up to £400 million a year. The 2008 NHS staff survey found 28 per cent of staff had felt unwell because of work-related stress over the previous 12 months. NHS Employers ran a campaign throughout 2006 to encourage employers to carry out risk assessments and change their policies and procedures to reduce workplace stress. It also included information to help staff spot the signs of stress and offered advice on what to do about it.

The 2008 staff survey found that 23 per cent of staff felt they had been bullied or harassed. The NHS has taken strong steps to eliminate this kind of behaviour in the workplace but it is clear that problems persist. In 2007 NHS Employers developed model policy, employer and staff guidance, HR toolkits and communications materials for employers and staff to tackle bullying.

# 09 Evidence, research and development

Policy for health and healthcare must be based on reliable evidence about the population's needs and what will work best to meet them. Such evidence originates from many types of research, covering prevention of ill health, promotion of health, disease management, patient care, delivery of healthcare and its organisation, as well as public health and social care. Conducting research to improve health and medical treatments was one of the NHS's founding principles, and the UK health research system has an even longer tradition of excellence: the Medical Research Council has funded 27 Nobel prize-winners since it was founded in 1913. This reputation, combined with the existence of a national health service, attracts high levels of research and development (R&D) investment from the pharmaceutical and biotechnology industries – an important part of the UK 'knowledge economy'.

Several recent developments have been designed to ensure the UK maintains this pre-eminence. They include a new strategy for research in the NHS in England, *Best research for best health*, new organisations to help achieve the strategy and the creation of the UK Clinical Research Collaboration. The Government's ambition is to raise the level of R&D spending to 2.5 per cent of GDP by 2014. It wants the NHS to foster a culture that pioneers new treatments so it becomes a hive of research activity attracting the best researchers in the world.

## Government, strategy and infrastructure

### Department of Health's role
The DH invests in research to support Government objectives for public health, health services and social care, as well as contributing to the Government science strategy. To deliver these objectives, the DH:
• identifies needs and priorities for R&D in health and social care
• persuades other organisations to fund R&D that falls within their remits
• provides support funding for non-commercial research in NHS organisations
• funds and manages R&D not picked up by others
• supports synthesis of research and dissemination of findings to users
• uses research in policy-making
• contributes to wider Government science and technology strategy.

The DH's current research priority areas are:

- cancer
- mental health
- coronary heart disease
- ageing and older people
- public health
- genetics
- diabetes.

**Key text: _Best research for best health_**

The Government's health research strategy, _Best research for best health_, sets the direction for NHS R&D. Launched in 2006, its five-year goals are to:

- establish the NHS as an internationally recognised centre of research excellence
- attract, develop and retain the best research professionals to conduct people-based research
- commission research focused on improving health and care
- strengthen and streamline systems for research management and governance
- act as sound custodians of public money for public good.

As part of the strategy:

- every patient in England will have access to clinical trials and the chance to take part in studies involving new medical therapies
- approval for research projects will be streamlined to avoid bureaucracy, and a national expert advice line will advise researchers on the law
- through the National Programme for IT, data collected from the NHS will meet researchers' needs and enable patients to access opportunities to participate in clinical trials
- research programmes will be expanded and world-leading research centres established to drive progress in biomedicine and NHS service quality and safety
- researchers of all disciplines and levels will be supported by the National Institute for Health Research with mentoring and training for career development.

**Further information**

_Best research for best health: a new national health research strategy – the NHS contribution to health research in England_, DH, January 2006.

## National Institute for Health Research

The National Institute for Health Research (NIHR) has been set up to deliver the Government's R&D strategy. Its goal is to create a health research system in which the NHS supports outstanding individuals working in world-class facilities and conducting leading-edge research focused on the needs of patients and the public. The NIHR:

- supports individuals carrying out and participating in research
- commissions and funds research
- provides facilities for a thriving research environment
- creates unified, streamlined and simple knowledge management systems.

Its programmes are:

- applied research – grants for leading researchers with an impressive track record; the first were made in mental health, medicines for children, diabetes, stroke and dementias, neurodegenerative diseases and neurology
- research for patient benefit (RfPB) – addresses issues of importance to the NHS, including research into everyday practice
- invention for innovation research – aims to accelerate the NHS's take-up of proven new treatments and devices
- research for innovation, speculation and creativity (RISC) – for speculative and radical health research proposals that could lead to a step-change in patient care
- public health research (PHR) – on the benefits, costs, acceptability and wider effect of non-NHS interventions such as prevention of obesity in children and speed humps for preventing road accidents
- health services research (HSR) – intended to lead to improved service quality and patient safety through better planning and provision
- health technology assessment (HTA) – to ensure healthcare professionals, NHS managers, the public and patients have the latest information on the costs, effectiveness and impact of health technology developments
- service delivery and organisation (SDO) – research on the way health services are organised and delivered by the NHS
- NHS physical environment research and development – improving the way property and facilities are managed and maintained and promoting safe, high-quality and best-value design
- research capacity development – provides support, guidance and academic training for the next generation of researchers.

Since its inception, NIHR has set up clinical research networks to support clinical trials throughout England and promote patient and public involvement in health research. They have increased numbers taking part in clinical trials, and improved their speed, quality and co-ordination. The UK now has the highest national per capita rate of cancer trial participation in the world. There are six topic-specific networks for cancer, dementia and neuro-degenerative diseases, diabetes, medicines for children, mental health and stroke. Another covers primary care. NIHR is setting up a comprehensive NHS research network covering all other diseases and areas of need.

NIHR is investing £468 million over five years in 11 biomedical research centres investigating major causes of illness and death such as cancer, heart disease, asthma, HIV, mental illness, blindness, childhood diseases and ageing. The centres are partnerships between the NHS and universities in London, Oxford, Cambridge, Liverpool and Newcastle. They will be complemented by 12 biomedical research units that will take advances in medical research into the hospital. Their work will focus on areas traditionally receiving limited research funding, including gastrointestinal and liver disease, deafness, musculoskeletal disease and nutrition. They will receive £45 million over the next four years.

The Next Stage Review recommended designating a small number of partnerships between research, education and health services as academic health science centres. This is now underway, guided by an international peer review panel. They will benefit mainly from recognition and prestige rather than extra funding, enabling them to compete with internationally renowned centres such as Harvard and Johns Hopkins in the USA and Sweden's Karolinska Institute.

NIHR's annual budget incorporates all previously existing funds for NHS research in England, as well as NHS funding that supports clinical research and academics.

**Further information**
*Transforming health research: the first two years – National Institute for Health Research progress report 2006–2008*, DH, January 2008.
www.nihr.ac.uk

NHS Evidence is a web portal providing access to authoritative clinical and non-clinical evidence and best practice. Announced in the Next Stage Review, launched in April 2009 and hosted by NICE, NHS Evidence aims to be a 'one-stop shop' for health information for the NHS in England. Drawing on local, national and international sources, it covers primary research, summarised clinical evidence, policy documents, commissioning and drugs. Information from the British National Formulary is a key element. A quality assessment process ensures the best information is 'kite-marked'. NHS Evidence is designed for professionals but is accessible to the public, and is intended to be as easy to use as any internet search engine.

### Office for Strategic Co-ordination of Health Research (OSCHR)

The Cooksey Report (see page 210) recommended setting up OSCHR to take an overview of the budgetary division and research strategy of both the Medical Research Council and NIHR.

OSCHR has been jointly established as a government office by the DH and the Department for Innovation, Universities and Skills. Its role is to work with the MRC and NIHR to develop a single integrated health research strategy covering all areas of health research. Key functions are to:

- work with officials to set the Government's health research strategy, taking into account advice on priorities and needs from NIHR, its equivalents in Scotland, Wales and Northern Ireland, the MRC and the NHS
- set a budget for the strategy and submit a single bid to the Treasury
- communicate the UK's health priorities to the pharmaceutical and bioscience sectors
- monitor delivery of the strategy against objectives and report to Parliament on progress
- encourage a stronger partnership between Government, health industries and charities.

### Further information

*OSCHR: chairman's first progress report,* HM Government, November 2008.

### Milestones in NHS research

During its 61-year history, the NHS has played a central role in health R&D. Major discoveries involving the NHS include:

- in 1950, Sir Richard Doll and Sir Austin Bradford Hill discovered a link between smoking and lung cancer; in 1954, 80 per cent of UK adults smoked – now only 26 per cent do
- in 1962, orthopaedic surgeon Sir John Charnley was the first to perform a total hip replacement at Wrightington Hospital, Wigan; the NHS now carries out more than 62,000 hip replacements a year
- in 1978, the world's first IVF baby, Louise Brown, was born in Oldham General Hospital; more than 1 million 'test tube babies' have been born since
- in the 1990s, Professor Lesley Regan of St Mary's Hospital, London, discovered that 15 per cent of women who suffered recurrent miscarriages carried antibodies in their blood that made it prone to clotting; she found that by treating such women with aspirin and heparin their rate of live births rose from 10 to 70 per cent.

**Further information**

*60 years of research in the NHS benefiting patients*, NIHR, June 2008.

## Funding R&D

### Who funds R&D?

The DH is the largest single public sector contributor, but it is not the only funder of UK health and social care research. The funding councils, research councils – especially the MRC – and research charities all play significant roles. Industry is a major investor in healthcare R&D. The health departments in Scotland, Wales and Northern Ireland also support health and social care R&D. Other government departments provide research funding too.

### CSR funding

The comprehensive spending review in 2007 resulted in full funding for the Cooksey Report recommendations (see page 210). Public funding for health research will rise to £1.7 billion, with ring-fenced funding for NIHR of £1 billion by 2010–11. This level of funding is intended to support an unprecedented growth in the number of NHS clinical trials in England.

## Programme grants for applied research

A key strand of the R&D strategy is to support applied health research addressing the NHS's priorities and needs. NIHR's programme grants for applied research funding are therefore designed to:

- provide evidence to improve health outcomes through promoting health, preventing ill health, and disease management, particularly for conditions causing significant disease burden, where other research funders may not be focused or insufficient funding is available
- enable NHS trusts to tackle areas of high priority or need for health
- provide stability of funding to support long-term development of top-quality applied research groups in the NHS.

Key text: **Cooksey Report**

Sir David Cooksey's report in 2006 reviewed the institutional arrangements for health research and highlighted a number of health challenges facing the UK and the rest of the world, including cancer, mental health, chronic and degenerative disease, nutrition, diet and lifestyle, cardiovascular diseases and infectious diseases such as malaria, TB and HIV/AIDS.

Cooksey recommended bringing together the research budgets of the MRC and the DH to achieve better co-ordination of health research and more coherent funding arrangements. He also called for the establishment of the Office for Strategic Co-ordination of Health Research to act as a central co-ordinating body for health research.

**Further information**

*A review of UK health research funding*, HM Treasury, December 2006.

## Research organisations

Apart from the main statutory bodies, other organisations play an important part in gathering and analysing evidence and promoting R&D.

### UK Cochrane Centre

The UKCC was established in 1992 by the NHS R&D programme 'to facilitate and co-ordinate' systematic reviews of randomised controlled trials. It is now one of 12 Cochrane Centres around the world which provide the infrastructure for co-ordinating the Cochrane Collaboration, an international, not-for-profit, independent organisation, dedicated to making up-to-date, accurate information about the effects of healthcare readily available worldwide. The Cochrane Library is a regularly updated collection of evidence-based medicine databases, including the Cochrane database of systematic reviews, which provides high-quality information to professionals and the public.

www.cochrane.co.uk

## UK Clinical Research Collaboration
The UK Clinical Research Collaboration brings together the NHS, research funders, industry, regulatory bodies, Royal Colleges, patient groups and academe to promote high-quality clinical research. Its main activities are:
- developing a comprehensive infrastructure to underpin clinical research
- building an expert research workforce to support clinical research
- developing incentives for research in the NHS
- streamlining regulations and governance
- developing a co-ordinated approach to research funding.

www.ukcrc.org

## UK Clinical Research Network
Set up in 2005, UKCRN aims to speed up access to the best treatment as well as improve the integration and co-ordination of research, enhancing its quality. It also seeks to increase the number of NHS organisations, healthcare professionals and patients actively involved in research studies and strengthen links with industry.

www.ukcrn.org.uk

## Centre for Reviews and Dissemination
Part of York University and set up in 1994, CRD claims to be the largest group in the world engaged exclusively in evidence synthesis in the health field. It undertakes systematic reviews that evaluate the effects of health and social care interventions and the delivery and organisation of healthcare. CRD maintains databases, provides an inquiry service and disseminates research results to NHS decision-makers.

www.york.ac.uk/inst/crd

## Health Services Research Network
HSRN aims to connect all universities, commercial and professional organisations, charities and NHS bodies with an interest in research underpinning improvements in how health services are financed, organised, planned and delivered, including health technology assessments and health policy research. It seeks to influence policy-

makers and managers to support better use of research, campaigns for secure funding for health services research and for measures to improve the careers of those engaged in it.
www.nhsconfed.org/HSRN

## SDO Network
This is a network of NHS organisations supporting research, evaluation and innovation. It aims to provide services customised to the needs of senior, middle and new NHS managers to help their organisations develop leading-edge services. It does this by facilitating their access to and use of the latest health services research. The network provides a safe place for managers to work and reflect with their peers, academics and leaders from the private sector on the best ways of using research knowledge to improve the services they manage. The network is provided by the NHS Confederation.
www.nhsconfed.org/sdonetwork

**Spotlight on policy: Health Innovation Council**
The Next Stage Review recommended setting up a Health Innovation Council with a fund of up to £100 million to help the NHS develop and deploy hi-tech healthcare such as medical devices and diagnostics. Drawing from the NHS, academe and industry, it supports the discovery and development of new products and techniques, encouraging the adoption of cost-effective innovations, especially in:
• pharmaceuticals
• other medical technologies
• clinical practice
• delivery models of service
• management.

HIC is intended to complement NICE and the NHS Institute for Innovation and Improvement.

# 10 Information technology

In his 2002 report on the NHS's long-term future (see page 182), Sir Derek Wanless made several key recommendations for IT in the NHS:

- doubling the IT budget and ensuring it is not used to subsidise other services
- stringent, centrally managed national standards for data and IT
- better management of IT implementation, including a national programme.

Wanless commented: 'Without a major advance in the effective use of ICT, the health service will find it increasingly difficult to deliver the efficient, high-quality service which the public will demand. This is a major priority which will have a crucial impact on the health service over future years.'

A modern IT infrastructure is vital to improving patient safety and enabling choice, helping clinicians to work efficiently and allowing them access to patient information promptly and securely.

Since the Wanless Report, the Government has made major investments in NHS IT, devising an ambitious national programme to install systems throughout the service and setting up an agency, Connecting for Health, to deliver it. The Next Stage Review highlighted challenges 'in an age of information and connectivity', and the information requirements arising from it were examined in a parallel informatics review.

## National Programme for IT

### Why have a national programme?
The National Programme for IT (NPfIT), launched in 2002, is more extensive than any other IT programme in the world, and represents the largest ever single IT investment in the UK. It is intended to ensure that lost records, inconvenient appointments and delayed test results become a thing of the past. National systems are replacing organisations' separate IT systems that did not communicate with each other. Once installed, the new IT infrastructure will connect more than 110,000 doctors, 390,000 nurses and 120,000 other healthcare professionals, giving patients access to their personal health and care information while transforming the way the NHS works. (NHSScotland has its own national eHealth IM&T strategy, see page 247; NHS Wales has its own approach, Informing Healthcare, see page 263; the health service in Northern Ireland has now embarked on a ten-year programme of investment in IT, see page 276.)

NPfIT's overall cost is expected to be £12.7 billion over ten years to 2013/14. Since it started, costs have increased by £678 million due to the purchase of increased functionality. In addition to national IT spending, trusts have increased their investment in – for example – payroll, finance and HR systems in line with the 2002 Wanless Report's recommendation that they should devote 4 per cent of their budgets to IT by 2008.

### Implementing NPfIT

Implementing NPfIT does not involve a 'big bang'. Systems and services are being gradually phased in, according to priorities and when NHS organisations are ready to implement them. However, the National Audit Office reported in 2008:

> Delivering NPfIT is proving to be an enormous challenge. All elements of the programme are advancing and some are complete, but the original timescales for the electronic care records service, one of the central elements of the programme, turned out to be unachievable, raised unrealistic expectations and put confidence in the programme at risk.

Nevertheless, it added that 'the original vision remains intact and still appears feasible'.

If full implementation is to succeed, the NHS must meet several challenges that the NAO identified as:
- achieving strong leadership and governance of the programme
- maintaining patients' confidence that records will be secure
- securing support and involvement from clinicians and other staff
- managing suppliers effectively
- deploying and using the systems effectively at local level.

Every hospital was using picture archiving and communications systems by the end of 2007, and deployment of the electronic booking service is almost complete. But the Care Records Service is unlikely to be fully deployed before 2014/15, four years later than planned. The software has taken much longer to develop than envisaged so some trusts have installed an interim system. Problems with the system for the North, Midlands and East area may still lead to further delay.

The Commons public accounts committee felt the departure from the programme of two of the original four local service providers had heightened risks, and was sceptical that the Care Records Service would be fully implemented by 2014/15. Deployment of the care record system

**Health informatics review**

The DH's health informatics review outlined the informatics requirements of the Next Stage Review, including the IT, processes, analytical tools and techniques, governance and skills needed.

It found the range and quality of information available needed to be enhanced and integrated into all aspects of health and social care, making proposals for clear central leadership and accountability. DH policy will in future include routine informatics assessments to ensure the information requirements of new policies are considered from the outset. In consulting 1,400 stakeholders, including patients, public and clinicians, the review discovered concerns about:

• ownership of strategy and future objectives
• potential future skills shortages
• getting maximum benefit from systems
• increasing trust in information and its management
• delivering effective solutions and closing gaps in data coverage
• improving access to information
• overcoming fragmented governance and reporting arrangements
• agreeing common standards.

The review found lack of progress with key aspects of NPfIT, particularly the Care Records Service, had caused major problems for trusts. As a result, trusts have since been allowed to implement interim local IT solutions if they are consistent with NPfIT's overall objectives and solutions. The review noted that the DH and NHS Connecting for Health (CFH) have important roles to play in developing e-learning and ensuring informatics is an integral part of basic training for new NHS staff. It also pledged a more strategic and co-ordinated approach to reporting and information requirements to reduce the burden of data collection.

**Further information**

*Health informatics review report*, DH, July 2008.
*Briefing 170: The 2008 health informatics review*, NHS Confederation, August 2008.

in a London acute trust has highlighted significant problems with the software that has raised further doubts about achieving this target.

A DH survey in 2007 found 67 per cent of nurses and 62 per cent of doctors expected the new systems to improve patient care. NPfIT was estimated to have saved £208 million for the NHS by 2006/07, projected to total £1.1 billion by 2013/14.

### Further information
*The National Programme for IT in the NHS: progress since 2006*, National Audit Office, May 2008.
*Second report of session 2008–09: the National Programme for IT in the NHS: progress since 2006*, House of Commons public accounts committee, January 2009.

## Who does what
The NPfIT Local Ownership Programme (NLOP) was devised in 2006 to enable NHS organisations to define their own IT priorities and align NPfIT with new information governance arrangements. Strategic health authorities and primary care trusts became accountable in 2007 for delivering NPfIT, with support from NHS Connecting for Health (NHS CFH), which is responsible for day-to-day operational management. A national programme board, chaired by the NHS chief executive is responsible for directing NPfIT. National clinical leads have been appointed to strengthen clinical authority within NPfIT.

To ensure relationships with local service providers continue effectively, NPfIT management boards have been established in three areas – London; the North, Midlands and East; and Southern.

In addition:
• three national application service providers are responsible for purchasing and integrating IT systems common to all users
• local service providers deliver IT systems and services locally for the three areas.

### Further information
*Better information, better health*, NHS CFH, April 2007.
*A practical guide to NHS Connecting for Health*, NHS CFH, June 2007.

NHS Connecting for Health is an agency of the Department of Health, set up in 2005. Its main role is to deliver NPfIT and maintain the business systems on which the NHS relies. It succeeded the NHS Information Authority, and was formed after the review of arm's-length bodies (see page 23). Its staff are drawn from across the NHS, civil service, academe and the private sector, and encompass management, IT, clinical and medical skills. It has nine prime contracts delivered by six suppliers, together with sub-contractors and other partners.

NHS CFH is delivering NPfIT in England only. Scotland, Wales and Northern Ireland are developing their own IT programmes, but NHS CFH recognises the importance of compatibility. The UK Information Management & Technology Forum has been set up to allow interaction between policy leads from all four UK countries. In addition, the Information Standards Board has representatives from each.
**www.connectingforhealth.nhs.uk**

## IT infrastructure

The NPfIT infrastructure includes:
- the NHS Care Records Service (CRS)
- GP2GP, allowing electronic health records to be transferred between practices
- Choose and Book, the electronic booking service
- Electronic Prescriptions Service (EPS)
- a national broadband IT network (N3)
- NHSmail, a central e-mail and directory service for the NHS
- NHSweb
- NHS Choices
- HealthSpace
- picture archiving and communications systems (PACS)
- IT supporting GP payments, including the Quality Management and Analysis System (QMAS).

### NHS Care Records Service

A single electronic record system to which all care providers have access is essential because patients attend various institutions at different times, encountering a range of care professionals and organisations including social care and the independent sector. The NHS Care Records Service will connect GPs and trusts in a single, secure national system, providing all 50 million NHS patients in England with an individual electronic care record detailing key treatments in the health service or social care.

Every patient will have a two-part care record. The detailed care record – held locally – will be formed from the detailed notes made by every healthcare professional who treats the patient; the summary care record – held nationally – will contain essential information selected from the detailed record, such as allergies or medication. Patients will be able to access their own summary care record using HealthSpace (see page 222). They may choose not to have a record created or not to have it shared, though so far few have done either.

Clinical need and patient wishes will decide who has access to records. Access to the computer system will only be allowed after training, and users must register to obtain an NHS 'smartcard' with a chip and personal identification number. Users must be directly involved in the care of the patient whose record they wish to access, and access will depend on their role: for example, a receptionist booking an appointment will only have access to basic information to identify a patient and make the booking. Every time someone accesses a patient's record, a note will be made of who, when and what they did. Patients will be able to request this information. A 'care record guarantee' sets out the principles governing storage and access to records for patients. The NHS CRS Registration Authority is responsible for registering and verifying the identity of NHS staff who need to access records.

A core data storage and messaging system, known as 'the Spine', is central to the CRS. In addition to storing patients' personal characteristics, summarised clinical information and security systems, this will offer a secondary users service providing anonymised data for business reports and statistics for research and planning.

Initially every patient was to have an electronic care record by 2010, but in 2008 the NAO noted 'considerable uncertainty' about when the CRS would be fully deployed. The first phase was completed during 2004, and included the infrastructure to enable booking of outpatient appointments and professionals to view basic patient information. An 'early adopter' programme to implement the summary care record began in 2007, involving five PCTs. By January 2009, 207,730 summary care records had been uploaded to the Spine, and 558,035 smartcard holders were registered and approved for access. Developing detailed care records has proved a 'far greater challenge' than anticipated, according to the NAO. It found 128 deployments had been made by March 2008.

The GP2GP project enables the electronic transfer of patients' healthcare records from one GP surgery to another. It is designed to ensure records are available to the new GP within 24 hours of a patient registering with their practice. By early 2009, there were 5,021 practices using GP2GP and had made 417,718 transfers.

### Further information
*The care record guarantee: our guarantee for NHS care records in England*, NHS CFH, 2007.
www.nhscarerecords.nhs.uk

## Choose and Book
Choose and Book, the electronic booking service, is designed to underpin the policy of enabling patients to choose which hospital to attend at a date and time to suit them. The software allows GPs and other primary care staff to make initial hospital or clinic outpatient appointments before the patient has left the surgery. This enables clinicians to track referrals more easily and conduct e-mail discussion about cases when necessary. It also provides more consistent, accurate and efficient referral information without the delays of paper correspondence. Choose and Book should reduce the chance of patients not turning up for appointments and improve clinical governance by providing an audit trail.

Between its introduction in 2004 and January 2009, over 12 million bookings had been made. Choose and Book was being used for about 50 per cent of NHS referral activity from GP surgery to first outpatient appointment. All hospitals and over 90 per cent of GP practices were using it, sending up to 28,000 referrals a day.
www.chooseandbook.nhs.uk

## Electronic prescription service
The electronic transmission of prescriptions programme is implementing the electronic prescription service (EPS) and integrating it with the NHS CRS. EPS will operate throughout England.

Prescriptions are transferred electronically to a pharmacist nominated by the patient. If a pharmacy has not been nominated, the patient is given an ePrescription to present at a pharmacy. This has a barcode which enables the pharmacist to obtain details of the prescription from the NHS CRS. The prescribed medication details are added to the patient's electronic record held by the NHS CRS. Electronic transmission will increase patient safety by reducing prescription errors and providing better information at the point of prescribing and dispensing. This creates the opportunity to reduce adverse drug events, where the patient responds poorly to medication. Over 155 million prescription messages had been transmitted electronically by January 2009, and EPS was being used for 24 per cent of the 1.3 million prescription issued daily. Almost 6,000 GP practices and 8,000 pharmacies were using EPS. Eventually other locations such as walk-in centres, dental practices and hospitals will be included.

## N3: the New National Network
N3 provides the entire NHS with fast broadband networking services, and forms the essential technical infrastructure for NPfIT's other major projects. It replaced the earlier NHSnet, saving £900 million over seven years, and is Europe's largest virtual private network. Clinicians can send high-quality images to specialists for remote diagnosis and use N3 for secure clinical messaging. It makes video conferencing and remote working easier, and saves on telephone costs by enabling NHS organisations to converge their voice and data networks. It is intended to be flexible enough for future needs and allow the NHS to take early advantage of improvements in technology. Connections to N3 started in 2004. About 1.2 million NHS employees have access, including all GP practices.
www.n3.nhs.uk

## NHSmail
NHSmail is a secure national e-mail and directory service for NHS staff in England and Scotland, developed specifically to meet the British Medical Association's requirements for clinical e-mail between NHS organisations. It provides a national directory of people in the NHS, containing the name, e-mail addresses, telephone numbers, name and address of their organisation, and information about departments, job roles and specialties. Staff are assigned an e-mail address that moves with them if they change job or location within the NHS. By January 2009, there were 400,000 staff registered and an average of 983,152 messages passed through the system daily. When complete it will have 1 million users, making it the world's largest private, single-domain e-mail service.

## NHSweb

Websites can be hosted exclusively on N3 for NHS use, and are described as being on NHSweb as opposed to being on the worldwide web. NHSweb also hosts intranets for individual NHS organisations. Users connected to other networks are blocked at the firewall and cannot access NHSweb sites, although they may send e-mails.

## NHS Choices

NHS Choices is the NHS's online service for the public, providing information on health conditions, treatments, healthy living and health services. Since integration with NHS Direct Online in October 2008, NHS Choices provides a single 'front door' for the public to all NHS online services and information through the country's biggest health website. This includes information to help people find services and compare hospitals. NHS Choices receives 5.5 million visits a month.

### Further information
*NHS Choices: delivering for the NHS*, DH, April 2008.
www.nhs.uk

## HealthSpace

HealthSpace is a secure website where patients can store personal health information online, such as height, weight and blood pressure. It is free and available for all NHS patients living in England aged 16 and over. Anyone living in an area that has adopted a care record system can view their summary care record through an Advanced Healthspace account.
www.healthspace.nhs.uk

## NHS number

The NHS number is the common currency of NHS information and fundamental to NPfIT. Babies born in England and Wales are allocated an NHS number at birth. It is a unique identifier that provides a common link between a patient's records – electronic and manual – across the NHS. It consists of ten digits: the first nine are the identifier and the tenth is a check digit used to confirm the number's validity. It is the cornerstone of the move towards an electronic health record, and enables disparate information to be collated into a comprehensive record of a person's health.

## National Library for Health (NLH)

The National Library for Health is a comprehensive web resource that brings together all NHS library and information services. It aims to collect in one place trusted, authoritative information resources, providing seamless access to the best available evidence wherever, and whenever, it is needed. Its services include:

- web-based specialist libraries for major health priority areas
- clinical information and summaries of evidence
- bibliographic databases and contents tables to support research
- collections of full-text e-journals and e-books
- a collection of freely available medical images
- current awareness services
- clinical question answering

NLH is part of the NHS Institute for Innovation and Improvement.
www.library.nhs.uk

## PRIMIS+

PRIMIS+ (formerly Primary Care Information Services) provides training and assistance to information and data-quality facilitators employed by PCTs or local health informatics services. These facilitators then 'cascade' their knowledge and skills to local GPs and practice staff. PRIMIS+ is managed by the Information Centre for Health and Social Care and based at Nottingham University's division of primary care.
www.primis.nhs.uk

**Key organisation: National Information Governance Board**
NIGB was set up in 2008 to ensure patient data is stored and used securely. It promotes consistent standards for information governance across health and social care, and tackles the ethical and legal interpretation and application of policies, procedures and guidance. It has issued guidance on topics such as the children's summary care record, locums' access to NPfIT systems and the security of NHS data.
www.nigb.nhs.uk

# Collecting and using data

Collecting data from frontline NHS organisations is necessary to ensure patient safety and provide accountability. But it became apparent that the burden of data collection had grown disproportionately, with much duplication and overlap to satisfy the demands of inspection and regulatory bodies. The DH therefore introduced a policy of collecting only essential data, designed to ensure that:

• collections fit with national policies
• requests for the same information are not repeated
• NHS organisations can complete these in as little time as possible.

During 2004/05 the DH examined data requirements and identified 61 central collections to be eliminated or streamlined. Since then it says data collection has been reduced by 28 per cent for the NHS overall, with about half of all central collections being stopped or cut in size for foundation trusts. In 2007 the Government set a target to reduce the data burden from central departments on frontline staff by 30 per cent by 2010. By October 2008, the burden had been cut by 10 per cent, according to the Information Centre.

The DH's Review of Central Returns (ROCR) team is charged with minimising central data demands on the NHS. It regularly reviews all information requirements and approves requests for information – including one-off surveys – taking account of the NHS effort involved in supplying the data requested. Only collections that have been through this process are added to the list of authorised central returns. If a request does not contain an ROCR number, NHS staff do not need to complete it. Even the need for data to answer parliamentary questions or support public expenditure survey negotiations is not a justification in itself for ROCR support.

The DH has developed UNIFY to act as a single 'warehouse' for information previously recorded on several local systems to meet different reporting requirements. Once data is captured, it now needs to be input only once, via NHSweb. This frees the NHS from multiple requests for additional information.

**Further information**
*Review of NHS data collections 2005*, DH/Information Centre, July 2006.

**Information Centre for Health and Social Care**
The Information Centre for Health and Social Care is a special health
authority that collects data from across health and social care, analyses it
and converts it into useful information.

Set up in 2005, it aims 'to be the recognised source of authoritative
comparative data, providing an independent perspective on the quality,
validity and application of information'. It is attempting to simplify and
streamline data collection processes, and reduce the time spent annually
on data collection in the NHS. Recent projects have included:
- enabling NICE to check prescribing patterns for compliance with its
  guidelines
- providing information to support patient choice
- integrating independent sector and NHS information
- helping SHAs use financial data more effectively
- promoting clinicians' use of information
- improving social care information.

**www.ic.nhs.uk**

# 11 The NHS in Scotland

The NHS in Scotland has abolished the structure which was a legacy of the internal market of the 1990s, replacing it with an integrated system that stresses collaboration and co-operation between organisations rather than competition. While variations in the NHS's structure and policy emphasis have always existed in different parts of the UK, they have become more prominent since devolution, especially in Scotland.

## The structure of NHSScotland

Ultimate responsibility for the NHS in Scotland lies no longer with Westminster but with the Scottish Parliament, and specifically the Scottish Government's cabinet secretary for health and well-being. The Scottish Government Health Directorates have strategic responsibility for the service. A range of special health boards provide services nationally, while locally 14 NHS boards both plan and provide services. Community health partnerships manage primary and community health services.

### The Scottish Parliament

The Scottish Parliament at Holyrood opened in 1999 with powers devolved from the UK Parliament covering matters that include health, social work, education, housing and local government. Its 129 members (MSPs) can therefore pass primary and secondary legislation affecting Scotland on a range of domestic issues. Issues concerning Scotland that have a UK or international impact are dealt with by the UK Parliament in Westminster. These 'reserved matters' include foreign affairs and defence, but also certain health-related issues:
• professional regulation
• abortion
• human fertilisation
• genetics
• control and safety of medicines.

The UK Parliament can also make laws that will apply to Scotland on any subject, but does not normally legislate on devolved matters without the consent of the Scottish Parliament.

Committees play a central part in the Parliament's work, taking evidence from witnesses, scrutinising legislation and conducting inquiries. The health and sport committee considers health policy and matters such as community care, public health and food safety, as well as sport. It is responsible for considering any proposed legislation that falls within its remit. This includes legislation setting out the Scottish Government's budget proposals for each financial year. The committee also commissions research, conducts inquiries and considers petitions submitted by the public. It has eight members, assigned between the parties on a proportional basis.

In addition, some of the Parliament's seven mandatory committees take an interest in NHSScotland: for example, the finance committee is concerned with public expenditure and how the Scottish Government's budget is spent, while the audit committee holds NHS boards to account for how they spend taxpayers' money and ensures public funds are spent effectively.

The Scotland Office, led by the Secretary of State for Scotland, represents Scottish interests in the UK Government and Parliament. There are 59 MPs at Westminster representing Scottish constituencies.

www.scottish.parliament.uk
www.scotlandoffice.gov.uk

### The Scottish Government
The devolved Scottish Government's relationship with the Scottish Parliament is similar to the relationship between the UK Government and the UK Parliament at Westminster. Members of the Scottish Government are chosen from the party or parties holding the largest number of seats in the Parliament. The Scottish Government was known as the Scottish Executive from its formation following devolution until after the elections in May 2007 when it was renamed by the current administration.

The Scottish Government is led by a First Minister, elected by the Scottish Parliament, who appoints a six-strong cabinet of Scottish ministers. Although the civil service in Scotland remains part of the UK civil service, its civil servants are accountable to Scottish ministers, who are themselves accountable to the Scottish Parliament. The Scottish Government administers an annual budget of over £30 billion.

www.scotland.gov.uk

## Scottish Government Health Directorates

The Scottish Government Health Directorates are responsible for NHSScotland as well as for developing and implementing health and community care policy. These directorates cover:

- Office of the chief medical officer
- chief nursing officer
- health delivery
- health finance
- health workforce
- healthcare policy and strategy
- primary and community care
- housing and regeneration
- public health and health improvement
- well-being.

They provide the statutory and financial framework for NHSScotland and hold it to account for its performance. The Scottish Government has discretion to intervene if serious problems arise locally.

On its election in May 2007, the Scottish Government created a new, expanded Health and Wellbeing portfolio, adding housing, community regeneration, equality and anti-poverty strategies and sport to the traditional health ministerial responsibilities. This is intended to ensure co-ordinated cross-cutting policy and action to address the root causes of ill health and inequalities in health status in Scotland.

Health and Wellbeing has three ministers: the cabinet secretary for health and well-being, the minister for public health and the minister for communities and sport. The director general health, as well as having overall responsibility for this expanded remit, is the chief executive of NHSScotland, and is accountable to ministers for the efficiency and performance of the service.

Scotland's chief medical officer is the Scottish Government's principal medical adviser, with direct access to ministers. The CMO is also head of the Scottish Medical Civil Service. The post has direct involvement in developing health policy, including prevention, health promotion, health protection and harm reduction. The CMO has lead responsibility for issues such as clinical effectiveness, quality assurance, accreditation and research, and covers the spectrum of health-related issues ranging from public health policy to NHS operations.

## Special health boards

Eight special health boards provide services nationally. These are:

- **National Waiting Times Centre**, comprising the Golden Jubilee National Hospital and the Beardmore Hotel and Conference Centre, both in Clydebank near Glasgow and bought from the private sector in 2002. The hospital carries out only elective procedures in key specialties to reduce waiting times. The NHS-owned four-star Beardmore Hotel has 168 bedrooms and a 170-seat auditorium, and is a national NHS and public sector conference facility.
  www.nhsgoldenjubilee.co.uk
  www.thebeardmore.com

- **NHS 24**, which provides 24-hour telephone access (0845 242424) to medical advice from clinical professionals and acts as a referral point to local out-of-hours services.
  www.nhs24.com

- **NHS Education for Scotland**, which designs, commissions and provides training and lifelong learning for NHSScotland's workforce.
  www.nes.scot.nhs.uk

- **NHS Health Scotland**, which support organisations, policy-makers, communities and individuals to take action to improve health and reduce health inequalities.
  www.healthscotland.com

- **NHS Quality Improvement Scotland**, the lead organisation in improving healthcare quality by setting, monitoring and reporting on standards and advising on clinical practice.
  www.nhshealthquality.org

- **Scottish Ambulance Service**, which employs over 3,000 staff.
  www.scottishambulance.com

- **State Hospitals Board for Scotland**, which cares for mentally ill patients needing treatment under secure conditions.
  www.tsh.scot.nhs.uk

- **National Services Scotland**, which provides specialist legal services, counter-fraud services, health statistics, screening programmes, family health service payments and patient registration. It also monitors clinical standards, as well as overseeing Scottish Healthcare Supplies, the Scottish National Blood Transfusion Service and Health Protection Scotland, which carries out surveillance of communicable diseases, environmental health hazards and public health.
  www.nhsnss.org

## Scottish NHS board areas

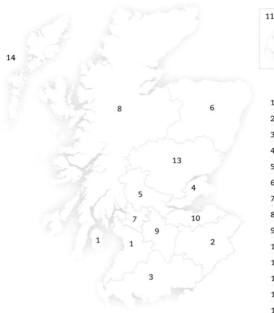

1 NHS Ayrshire and Arran
2 NHS Borders
3 NHS Dumfries and Galloway
4 NHS Fife
5 NHS Forth Valley
6 NHS Grampian
7 NHS Greater Glasgow
8 NHS Highland
9 NHS Lanarkshire
10 NHS Lothian
11 NHS Orkney
12 NHS Shetland
13 NHS Tayside
14 NHS Western Isles

## NHS boards

NHSScotland abolished trusts in 2004 in favour of local single-system working based on 14 (originally 15) NHS boards (11 mainland and three island boards). This was intended to instil shared aims, common values and clear lines of accountability while breaking down traditional barriers between primary and acute care.

NHS boards are mainly responsible for:
• protecting and improving their population's health
• delivering hospital, community and primary care services
• developing a local health plan to address health priorities and needs
• allocating resources according to the board's strategic objectives
• performance management of the local health system.

Boards have a statutory duty to take part in regional and national planning as part of regional planning groups. The three island health boards – Western Isles, Orkney and Shetland – are being strengthened

**Elected health boards**

MSPs look set to back a Scottish Government bill to introduce elections for health boards and allow members of the public to stand. The idea appeared in Labour's 2003 manifesto for the Scottish Parliament, but was not taken forward; a later attempt to introduce it in a member's bill was defeated in early 2007. Direct elections to NHS boards have been a longstanding policy of the Scottish National Party and appeared again in its 2007 manifesto.

Key proposals include:
- elected members – including local authority representatives and those directly elected by the public – would form a majority; ministers would appoint the chair and other members as at present
- pilot elections would be held and evaluated before full implementation
- elections would be held every four years on a proportional representation basis, with a single ward covering the whole health board area
- the voting age would be lowered to 16 for health board elections.

The Scottish Government and the bill's supporters believe that strengthening the NHS's local democratic accountability would improve public engagement and increase trust in decision-making processes. Opponents argue that boards could become dominated by candidates pursuing a narrow agenda, damaging public engagement.

Subject to the bill's progress at Holyrood, the first pilot elected boards would be chosen in 2010 and last for at least two years to test the full range of issues.

**Further information**
*Consultation document: local healthcare bill*, Scottish Government, January 2008.
*7th Report, 2008 (Session 3): Stage 1 report on the Health Boards (Membership and Elections) (Scotland) Bill*, Scottish Parliament health and sport committee, December 2008.

through partnerships with mainland boards designed to allow the larger organisations to use their wider range of resources to support the island boards. For example, Orkney has partnered Grampian, which will provide support in public health, healthcare associated infections, financial analyst support, human resources and delivery of Orkney's clinical services strategy. Each is receiving an extra £250,000 a year for this.

All board members are currently appointed by Scottish ministers, although appointments of non-executives are overseen by the Office of the Commissioner for Public Appointments in Scotland. Members divide into three categories:
• non-executive lay members, including the board chair
• non-executive 'stakeholder' members
• executive members.

Boards have between five and nine non-executive lay members. The chair, who is appointed directly by ministers – not elected by board members – is always a non-executive lay person. Each NHS board includes, as full non-executive directors:
• an employee director
• the chair of the area clinical forum
• the chair of the community health partnership advisory forum
• a representative from the university medical school (where applicable)
• an elected council member from each local authority area covered by the board.

There is no limit to the number of members per board, and overall size and balance varies. The largest – Greater Glasgow and Clyde – has 32, while the three island boards have 13 to 15 each.

### Community health partnerships
CHPs were set up in April 2005 to manage primary and community health services and replace the 79 local healthcare co-operatives. The Scottish Government elected in 2007 has reaffirmed their central role in NHSScotland. They number 40, with every NHS board having at least one, while the largest board – Greater Glasgow and Clyde – has 10. CHPs act as a focus for integrating primary and specialist services locally, forging partnerships with local authorities and the voluntary sector. Several CHPs have developed particularly advanced partnership arrangements with local authority community care services, and have evolved into community health and care partnerships (CHCPs).

Boards are expected to devolve power and responsibility to frontline staff in CHPs. Each CHP has a director or general manager, as well as a chair who is either a health board non-executive director or local authority elected member. CHPs have evolved to replace the old primary care operating divisions within NHS boards, and are now the mechanism for designing, planning and delivering all community-based services. CHP directors and general managers are core members of a board's senior management team.

They must currently address three key policy areas:
• shifting the balance of care to more local settings
• reducing health inequalities
• improving the health of local people.

Within that overall agenda, their specific priorities are:
• better access to primary care
• taking a systematic approach to long-term conditions
• anticipatory care
• supporting people at home
• preventing avoidable hospital admissions
• more local diagnosis and treatment
• enabling discharge and rehabilitation
• improving specific health outcomes.

**Further information**
Association of CHPs **www.achp.scot.nhs.uk**

## Managed clinical networks

Managed clinical networks for a wide range of conditions became well established in Scotland before the rest of the UK. They are defined as:
> linked groups of health professionals and organisations from primary, secondary and tertiary care, working in a co-ordinated manner, unconstrained by existing professional and health board boundaries, to ensure equitable provision of high-quality clinically effective services throughout Scotland.

They are seen as an important way of integrating systems of care and developing clinical leadership. Managed care networks are a development of the concept, designed to cross boundaries between the NHS and social work departments. The Scottish Government has pledged to encourage expansion of managed clinical networks as part of its health strategy. It plans to provide 'national leadership and resources' to set up networks for respiratory and neurological conditions. It envisages some networks recruiting staff and leading changes to specialist children's services, neurosurgery and laboratories.

## Scottish Health Council

The Scottish Health Council exists to ensure the views of patients and the public are properly taken into account by NHS boards. It assesses how boards are involving patients in decisions about health services, develops examples of best practice in public involvement and helps patients give feedback to boards about their experiences of services. Although part of NHS Quality Improvement Scotland, the council has its own identity and responsibilities with a national office in Glasgow and local offices in each board area, where most of its staff are based. Members of the community are appointed to serve on a local advisory council for each NHS board area. www.scottishhealthcouncil.org

## Scottish Medicines Consortium (SMC)

The Scottish Medicines Consortium, an independent group within NHS QIS, advises NHSScotland on the clinical and cost-effectiveness of all newly licensed medicines, new formulations of existing medicines and all new conditions the medicines will treat. It has 35 members, including healthcare professionals from NHS boards, pharmaceutical industry representatives and lay members. The SMC also has a database of 180 experts to advise on its decisions. The introduction of the SMC as a single advisory body has led to Scotland leading the UK in early, post-launch assessment of new medicines. It ensures that NHSScotland receives regular and standardised advice to enable it to introduce effective medicines as rapidly as possible. The SMC's decisions do not have statutory force, however, and it cannot insist that NHS boards prescribe a particular drug. www.scottishmedicines.org

## Strategy and policy

Bringing the NHS under the control of elected representatives in Scotland for the first time has resulted in new directions for the Scottish health service often quite distinct from policies pursued by the NHS in England. For example, NHSScotland has explicitly rejected market-based reforms introduced south of the border, and the Scottish Parliament voted in favour of providing free personal care for elderly people, for which charges are levied in England. But like the English NHS, NHSScotland has revised its position on 'topping up' to ensure patients paying for additional treatment or medication are not excluded from NHS care.

Divergence has become more marked now that opposing political parties control the administrations in Holyrood and Westminster. On forming the minority government in 2007, the Scottish National Party adopted five core strategic objectives on which it intends to focus government and public services. One of these is 'Healthier: help people to sustain and improve their health, especially in disadvantaged communities, ensuring better, local and faster access to health care.' Population health improvement and the reversal of health inequalities are strong policy themes across government.

Although the SNP supported the 2005 Kerr Report – which underpinned the previous Labour-led administration's health policy – and continues to use its core principles to inform most of its health strategy, since coming to power in 2007 it has also struck out in new directions. For example, it has:

- set up independent expert panels reporting to ministers to scrutinise major service reconfiguration decisions, 'with a general presumption against centralisation'
- reduced prescription charges as part of phased abolition by 2011
- abolished hospital car-parking charges
- legislated for direct elections to NHS boards
- consulted on legislation to exclude 'commercial companies with shareholders' holding primary medical services contracts
- banned new private contracts for hospital cleaning and catering services
- expanded GP surgery opening hours
- strengthened waiting-time targets, introducing an 18-week 'referral-to-treatment' standard
- introduced a major focus on healthcare-acquired infections, establishing a new reporting regime and pilots for national screening for MRSA
- announced a national uniform and dress code for staff from autumn 2009
- published a new health strategy, *Better health, better care*, and associated action plans.

## Recent milestones in Scottish health policy

*Designed to care* – 1997 white paper that announced primary care trusts and local healthcare co-ops were to be set up from 1999. PCTs were responsible for all primary and community health services, while LHCCs involved GPs in developing service provision.

**Health Act 1999** – ended the purchaser-provider split in Scotland, cutting trusts from 46 to 28 and abolishing GP fundholding.

*Our national health* – the Scottish NHS plan, published in December 2000, establishing unified NHS boards from 2001, under which trusts became integrated into a single local system, though remaining separate legal entities.

**Community Care and Health (Scotland) Act 2002** – enabled the NHS and local authorities to pool budgets for community care and created Joint Futures management bodies for community care services. Provides legislative backing for implementing free nursing and personal care.

*Partnership for care* – white paper, published in February 2003, that abolished trusts from 2004 and replaced LHCCs with community health partnerships.

*Fair to all, personal to each – the next steps for NHSScotland* – in December 2004, this set new targets for 'radical improvements' to the patient's journey through the system, particularly 18-week waiting-time targets.

*Building a health service fit for the future: a national framework for service change in the NHS in Scotland* (the Kerr Report) – published in May 2005 after a 14-month inquiry, this recommended improvements in long-term care, action on health inequalities, support for self-care, implementation of a new IT system, separation of planned care from emergencies and more community-based diagnostics, with specialist and complex care to be concentrated on fewer sites.

*Delivering for health* – published in October 2005, this was the Executive's response to the Kerr Report and set new priorities for NHSScotland based on it.

*Better health, better care: action plan* – the SNP minority government's plans for the NHS, published in December 2007 (see below).

*Equally well* – published in June 2008, this unveiled plans to tackle health inequalities by providing intensive support for young mothers, strengthening school nursing, improving play opportunities, creating jobs for people on health-related benefits, expanding checks on people with anxiety and depression and regularly assessing the health of people with learning disabilities.

### *Better health, better care* – the new Scottish health strategy

The Scottish Government's strategy for the health service lays great emphasis on seeing the public and staff as 'partners or co-owners' in 'a more mutual NHS', and promises not to change the funding model. It adds: 'In stressing public ownership through a more mutual approach, we distance NHSScotland still further from market orientated models'. Instead, 'co-operation and collaboration' are to be NHSScotland's guiding principles.

Among its plans are:
- a Patient's Rights Bill
- a charter of mutual rights, providing a clear statement of rights and responsibilities from the perspective of Government, staff and public
- to develop a 'participation standard' for boards to encourage patient and public involvement
- an annual 'ownership report' embodying the concept of mutuality, sent to every home
- extending GP practice opening hours
- piloting walk-in services through community pharmacies in shopping centres and at commuter points.

Proposals in the Patient's Rights Bill include:
- a 12-week legal waiting-time guarantee from when a patient is referred to hospital for surgery until the operation takes place, although 'this guarantee will operate within an overall referral to treatment patient journey of 18 weeks'
- independent patient rights officers for every health board area
- clearly defined systems of feedback and redress
- patients' responsibilities – for example, attending agreed appointments and offering feedback on services.

## Vital statistics: life expectancy 2004–06 (years)

|  | Men | Women |
|---|---|---|
| England | 77.2 | 81.5 |
| Scotland | 74.6 | 79.6 |
| Wales | 76.6 | 80.9 |
| Northern Ireland | 76.1 | 81.0 |

Source: UK health departments

## Managing performance

Local delivery plans agreed between the Scottish Government and each NHS board are based on the 'HEAT' key targets, which reflect ministers' priorities for the service. The HEAT objectives are:

- Health improvement – improving life expectancy
- Efficiency and governance – continually improving NHS efficiency and effectiveness
- Access to services – recognising patients' need for quicker and easier use of NHS services
- Treatment appropriate to individuals – ensuring patients receive high-quality services that meet their needs.

In 2007/08, NHSScotland achieved or exceeded most of its HEAT targets – especially for shorter waiting times – but failed to meet three. For 2009/10, 29 HEAT targets have been set, including:

- maximum waits of 31 days from decision-to-treat to first treatment for cancer patients, and 12 weeks for outpatient appointments and inpatient or day case treatment
- faster access to child and adolescent mental health services, and to treatment for drug misuse
- reducing hospital C. difficile infections by at least 30 per cent by 2011
- reducing energy consumption.

Each health board's performance is assessed through an annual review chaired by the cabinet secretary or health minister and held in public.

### Further information

*NHSScotland chief executive's annual report 2007/08*, Scottish Government, November 2008.

## Spotlight on policy: **Free personal care**

Uniquely in the UK, personal care services for people over 65 have been available free in Scotland since July 2002 (only nursing care is free in the rest of the UK). Eligibility depends on a needs assessment by the local authority, but is intended to be irrespective of income, capital assets, marital status or any care contribution by an unpaid carer. Personal care is defined as including help with personal hygiene, continence management, eating, simple treatments and personal assistance tasks.

Free personal care appears to have strong public support in Scotland, with 75 per cent saying the state should pay for those who need it. By 2006/07, 41,000 people were receiving free personal care at a cost of £224 million, a 21 per cent increase on the previous year.

In 2006, the Scottish Parliament health committee's care inquiry report found teething problems in implementing the policy but overall judged it to have been a success. In 2008, Audit Scotland said the policy had been launched without proper information about its costs or outcome measures, and it needed to be better planned, managed and funded: central funding was falling short of councils' costs by up to £63 million. Three-quarters of local authorities had introduced eligibility criteria.

Lord Sutherland's review commissioned by the Scottish Government recommended increased funding of £40 million and a more open and transparent system. He also criticised the UK Government for continuing to withhold attendance allowances previously paid to care home residents and currently valued at £30 million a year. All 12 of his recommendations were accepted by the Scottish Government, which provided the additional funding and is now working with local authorities to ensure 'greater consistency in how people access personal and nursing care services, including standard eligibility criteria and waiting times'.

### Further information

*A review of free personal and nursing care*, Audit Scotland, February 2008.
*Independent review of free personal and nursing care in Scotland*, Scottish Government, April 2008.

# Financing NHSScotland

## Sources of funding

General taxation and national insurance contributions form the main source of funding for NHSScotland, as they do for the NHS in the rest of the UK. Charges and receipts from land sales or other assets add comparatively small sums to the total. The Scottish Parliament is able to raise additional taxes, although it has yet to do so.

The Scottish Government intends to phase out prescription charges by April 2011, and in January 2009 it abolished car-parking charges at 14 hospitals, at a cost of £1.4 million. In the three hospitals where PFI contracts made abolition too expensive, health boards have been told to limit or reduce charges. Both measures are seen as reaffirming the principle that the NHS is 'free at the point of use'.

## Resource allocation

UK Government spending reviews, which take place every two years and cover a three-year cycle, determine the amount of public expenditure available for Scotland. Increases to the Scottish budget are made according to the population-based Barnett formula, introduced in1978 and modified slightly since devolution.

The Scottish Government then decides how this sum should be allocated among its departments, subject to the Scottish Parliament's approval. The health and community care budget has three main elements:
- hospital and community health services and family health services expenditure – the largest item, which includes payments to GPs, dentists, pharmacists and optometrists; the GP drugs bill; the costs of primary, acute and community health services
- other health services – including welfare foods, research and public health
- community care – central government spending on grants to voluntary organisations and on the Scottish Commission for the Regulation of Care; most community care spending is incurred by local authorities.

Part of the budget is top-sliced to fund national projects and Scottish Government spending on national programmes such as nurse education and training. Then resources are allocated to NHS boards under two categories:
- cash-limited unified budget – spent on hospital and community health services, including GP prescribing, and forming about 70 per cent of boards' discretionary allocation

- non-cash limited demand-led expenditure – spent on family health services provided by primary care contractors.

Allocations to boards, formerly made using the Arbuthnott weighted capitation formula devised in 2000, are to be made using a new formula being phased in from 2009/10. Devised by the NHSScotland resource allocation committee, the new formula:
- is built up from 6,500 small areas – 'datazones' – more sensitive to differences within communities, which will assist health board planning
- will keep better pace with changing board populations by using population projections
- is more sensitive to the costs of treating the very young and very old
- uses three measures to reflect additional healthcare needs and adjusts for underuse of services in deprived populations
- assesses the unavoidable costs of hospitals in remote and rural areas, taking account of the islands' special situation
- involves a new model of excess costs of community services using information from Scottish nursing, midwifery and allied health professionals.

**Further information**
*Delivering fair shares for health in Scotland: the report of the NHSScotland resource allocation committee*, NHSScotland, September 2007.
NHSScotland resource allocation committee **www.nrac.scot.nhs.uk**

**NHSScotland spending**
Scotland continues to spend more per head on health than the other UK countries (see page 9). NHSScotland's funding increased by 28 per cent in real terms between 2003/04 and 2007/08, but will increase by only 4 per cent between 2007/08 and 2010/11.

In 2007/08 NHSScotland spent £10.1 billion, a £26 million underspend against budget and its third consecutive underspend. It achieved £610 million in efficiency savings against a target of £531 million. In 2008/09 it is predicting a £64 million underspend. Boards must make 2 per cent efficiency savings a year for the next three years. NHSScotland's budget for 2009/10 is £11.09 billion.

Capital spending is set to grow from £430 million in 2007/08 to nearly £600 million in 2010/11, compared to £130 million in 2003/04.

Audit Scotland has warned that boards will face pressures from new pay deals for staff, rising drug and fuel prices and costs associated with reducing waiting times and service redesign, as well as full implementation of the European working-time directive.

**Further information**
*Financial overview of the NHS in Scotland 2007/08*, Audit Scotland, December 2008.

Spotlight on policy: **NHS cafés**
The first NHS-run café in Scotland opened at Glasgow Royal Infirmary in early 2009. Four other NHS Aroma cafés will open in Glasgow hospitals by the summer, and two in Highland – all wholly owned by the NHS. If successful, the cafés will be set up across Scotland. All profits will be reinvested in the NHS and outlets will be staffed by NHS employees. Fifty per cent of products will contain lower fat, sugar and salt.

## Staffing and human resources

### Staff numbers
A total of 165,551 people were employed in NHSScotland in September 2008 on a headcount basis, a 2.1 per cent increase on 2007. This includes:
• 12,534 doctors and dentists
• 67,965 nurses and midwives
• 9,242 allied health professionals (whole-time equivalent)
• 24,966 administrative staff
• 14,367 support staff.

### Workforce planning
About 70 per cent of NHSScotland's budget is allocated to the workforce. It published its first national workforce plan in 2006, detailing extra places for trainee GPs and hospital doctors and pledging to maintain numbers for pre-registration nursing and midwifery training. The Scottish Government updated this at the end of 2007 to fit in with its new health strategy, *Better health, better care*.

The rate of growth of NHSScotland's workforce is lower than the other UK countries', but its staff-to-population ratio is higher. Its workforce is also older than that of other UK countries.

### Further information

*National workforce plan 2006*, Scottish Executive Health Department, December 2006. *Better health, better care: planning for tomorrow's workforce today*, Scottish Government, December 2007.

## NHSScotland workforce by staff grouping (September 2008)

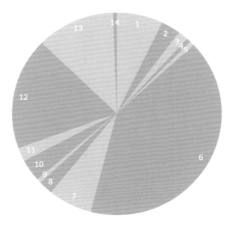

1   Medical (HCHS): 7.1%
2   General medical practitioners: 3%
3   Dental (HCHS): 1.6%
4   General dental services
5   Medical and dental support
6   Nursing and midwifery: 40.9%
7   Allied health professions: 6.8%
8   Other therapeutic services: 2.2%
9   Personal and social care
10   Healthcare science: 3.5%
11   Emergency services: 2.2%
12   Administrative services: 17.9%
13   Support services: 12.1%
14   Unallocated/not known

Source: ISD Scotland

## Vital statistics: NHS staff: a cross-border comparison (2005)

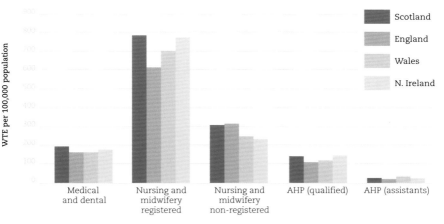

Source: Scottish Executive Health Department

## Staff Governance Standard

*Our national health*, the then Scottish Executive's health plan published in 2000, committed the NHS to becoming Scotland's best employer. The core standards for human resources practice in NHSScotland are set out in the Staff Governance Standard, which all NHS organisations must adhere to. This entitles all staff to be:

- well informed
- appropriately trained
- involved in decisions that affect them
- treated fairly and consistently
- provided with an improved and safe working environment.

The standard is supplemented by a series of best practice guidelines published by the Partnership Information Network Board. Topics include dignity at work, equal opportunities, family-friendly policies, personal development and dealing with employee concerns. NHS employers are expected to implement these fully. A third edition of the standard was published in 2007.

The NHSScotland staff opinion survey for 2008, in which 37 per cent of employees took part, found 73 per cent felt their job made good use of their skills and abilities, 80 per cent were clear about what they were expected to achieve, 76 per cent felt positive about support from colleagues and 77 per cent intended still to be working for the same NHS board in 12 months' time.

## Partnership forums

Each NHSScotland organisation has a local partnership forum to foster communication between staff, trade unions and managers. Each NHS board area has an area partnership forum. All NHS employers must develop a partnership agreement with staff and their representatives, which must contain – as a minimum – commitments to communication and consultation, access to information and board meetings and organisational change policies. Local partnership forums are mirrored nationally by the Scottish Partnership Forum, comprising senior NHS board managers, trade union national officers and health department representatives.

Every NHS board has an employee director as a full non-executive member. This is usually the elected staff representative from the local area partnership forum.

**Further information**

*Staff governance standard third edition for NHSScotland employees*, Scottish Executive, May 2007.

**Spotlight on policy: NHS uniform**

A new national uniform and dress code are being introduced for NHSScotland staff, 'to promote a professional corporate image and minimise the risk of infection'. Clinical staff will wear tunics in one of four shades of blue with navy trousers. Support staff such as porters and domestic and catering employees will wear tunics in one of two shades of green, with navy trousers. Staff who do not currently wear a uniform will not be required to do so. Staff should not wear uniform out of work.

The dress code applies to all staff, whether or not they are required to wear uniforms. They should:
• wear short-sleeved shirts or blouses
• not wear ties or white coats when providing patient care
• not carry pens or scissors in outside breast pockets
• tie back hair off the collar
• keep nails short and clean.

The Scottish Government is working with partners to develop a suitable uniform for administrative and clerical staff.

## Information technology in NHSScotland

### eHealth strategy 2008–11

A revised eHealth strategy was launched in 2008, to support the *Better health, better care* programme. It replaces a strategy from 2004, taking an 'incremental and pragmatic approach' and 'building on what exists and filling gaps where necessary'.

Its main features include:
• procurement of a patient management system for inpatient and outpatient scheduling and waiting-time management, online test ordering and results reporting plus scope for further modules such as A&E, theatres, electronic prescribing and maternity

- a replacement for GPASS (General Practice Administration System Scotland)
- a 'clinical portal' to act as a single online entry point for clinicians to access data about individual patients.

At the time of the strategy's launch:
- two health boards were implementing modern patient record systems that support clinical as well as administrative functions
- GPs were using the secure electronic messaging system for 17,000 outpatient referrals a month
- the emergency care summary contained information for over 5.1 million patients and was used 25,000 times a week with patient consent
- there was widespread use of the community health index number (CHI) on key clinical documents sent between GPs and acute hospitals and held on community-held case records
- NHSScotland's picture archiving and communications systems (PACS) were live in 21 sites, storing over 2 million images
- the ePharmacy programme was sending 1 million prescriptions a month from GP to community pharmacist then onwards for payment.

There are currently 96 national projects and programmes and over 160 local projects implemented by health boards within the national strategy. The eHealth budget is set to grow to £140 million by 2010/11.

**Further information**
*eHealth strategy 2008–2011*, Scottish Government/NHSScotland, June 2008.
www.ehealth.scot.nhs.uk

### Scotland's Health on the Web (SHOW)
This website is the official gateway to online information about NHSScotland.
www.show.scot.nhs.uk

# 12 The NHS in Wales

An awareness that Wales faces major health challenges has shaped its approach to providing care. It has high rates of cancer and heart disease and the highest proportion of elderly people of any of the four UK countries. Poverty levels are high in places, while services have to cater for a complex mix of rural, urban and valley areas.

## The structure of NHS Wales

The Welsh Assembly took over ultimate responsibility for the NHS in Wales from Westminster in 1999. Two departments within the Welsh Assembly Government have strategic responsibility for health, one focusing on the NHS and social care, the other on public health matters. After the election of a coalition government in May 2007, plans for significant structural change in the NHS in Wales were drawn up. NHS Wales, like NHSScotland before it, now intends to abolish the internal market and NHS trusts. Its current operating framework says: 'By the end of 2009/2010, the NHS in Wales will be very different from the picture a year earlier.'

### National Assembly for Wales

The National Assembly for Wales opened in 1999 and has 60 elected members (AMs). The UK Parliament devolved to it power to pass secondary legislation to enable it to develop and implement policies, make rules and regulations, set standards and issue guidance in areas that include health and social services, housing, local government, education and economic development. The Assembly's powers were extended by the Government of Wales Act 2006 so that it can now make its own legislation – known as Assembly measures – on devolved matters. Before making measures the Assembly needs to obtain 'legislative competence' on a case-by-case basis from the UK Parliament. This was designed to speed up the time it takes to make laws for Wales, as the Assembly can scrutinise and approve Welsh laws itself, rather than competing for space in the UK Parliamentary programme.

The Assembly provides democratic control of the management and performance of NHS Wales. It draws up strategic policies, sets priorities and allocates funds, but it is not currently able to raise extra taxes.

The Assembly's four scrutiny committees examine the expenditure, administration and policy of the Assembly Government and associated public bodies. Membership reflects the balance of political groups within the Assembly. The nine-member health, wellbeing and local government committee covers health and NHS Wales, local government and public service delivery.

Among the Assembly's ten mandatory committees, the audit committee scrutinises the expenditure of NHS Wales by examining reports on its accounts prepared by the Auditor General for Wales. The Wales Audit Office, created in 2005, combines the offices of the Audit Commission and the National Audit Office in Wales.

Regional committees represent the needs and interests of their localities, and convey issues of local concern to the full Assembly and to the scrutiny committees. There are five, made up of members from the relevant constituency and electoral region.

The Wales Office, led by the Secretary of State for Wales, represents Welsh interests in the UK Government and Parliament. There are 40 MPs at Westminster representing Welsh constituencies.

**Further information**
National Assembly for Wales **www.assemblywales.org**
Wales Office **www.walesoffice.gov.uk**
Wales Audit Office **www.wao.gov.uk**

## Welsh Assembly Government

The Welsh Assembly Government is the Assembly's executive body, led by the First Minister and an eight-strong cabinet that includes a minister for health and social services. The Government of Wales Act 2006 allows up to 12 ministers and deputy ministers, meaning the maximum size of the Welsh Assembly Government is 14, including the First Minister and Counsel General, who is the Government's chief legal adviser.

The First Minister is elected by AMs, and is therefore usually the leader of the largest party. Assembly elections are held every four years, the most recent being in May 2007 and resulting in a coalition of Labour and Plaid Cymru. Of the Assembly's 60 members, 40 are elected in constituencies using the first-past-the-post system; the other 20 are elected to represent the five regions of Wales using the list system.

## Department for Health and Social Services

The Department for Health and Social Services (DHSS) is led by the minister for health and social care and is responsible for:

- advising the Welsh Assembly Government on health and social care policies and strategies
- contributing to health and social care legislation
- funding the NHS and other health and social care bodies
- managing and supporting the delivery of health and social care services
- monitoring and promoting improvements in service delivery.

Other responsibilities include research and development, finance, human resources, information management and technology, capital and estates. The department's head is also chief executive of NHS Wales and the accounting officer for the health service. The department's constituent parts are:

- community, primary care, and health service policy directorate
- quality, standards and safety improvement directorate
- resources directorate
- children's health and social services directorate
- older people and long-term care policy directorate
- corporate management
- service delivery and performance
- strategy unit
- health and social services human resources
- Children and Family Court Advisory and Support Service in Wales.

The department's current priorities are:

- implementing local health, social care and well-being strategies to deliver integrated health and social care services
- improving health and quality of life
- reducing inequalities in personal health and access to services
- reducing waiting times, so that by December 2009 no one will wait longer than 26 weeks from GP referral to treatment
- implementing the quality plan for Wales to ensure safe, sustainable and accessible services
- implementing national standards of care for cancer, cardiac, children's, older people's, renal and diabetes services
- implementing policies which better reflect older people's needs
- implementing policies which safeguard children's needs.

# Wales: Local health boards

Welsh Ambulance Service
NHS Trust

Betsi Cadwaladr
University LHB

Powys LHB

Hywel Dda LHB

Abertawe
Bro Morgannwg
University LHB

Cwm
Taf
LHB

Aneurin
Bevan LHB

Cardiff & Vale
University LHB

Velindre
NHS Trust

Source: Welsh Assembly Government

## Department for Public Health and Health Professions

The DPHHP is also led by the minister for health and social care, but its director is the chief medical officer for Wales. Formed in 2007 from the Office of the Chief Medical Officer and the Office of the Chief Nursing Officer, its objectives are:

- to protect the health of the people in Wales and prepare for health emergencies
- to improve health and reduce health inequalities
- to provide professional leadership for health and social care.

To help achieve these, the department is:
- developing a public health strategic framework
- creating new public health structures.

The existence of the DPHHP as a separate entity within the Welsh Assembly Government reflects the high priority attached to improving public health in Wales. Two other national organisations involved in public health – the National Public Health Service and the Wales Centre for Health – are soon to be replaced. A 2006 review recommended a 'unifying public health strategy', and under NHS Wales' structural reforms a unified public health organisation will be created.

### Restructuring NHS Wales
The policy document, *One Wales* (see page 257), drawn up after the 2007 Assembly election, committed the coalition government to abolishing the internal market in NHS Wales. In 2008 the coalition proposed restructuring the health service to achieve this and to cut the number of NHS organisations.

Plans will involve abolishing 21 of the 22 local health boards set up in 2004 and replacing them with six newly constituted ones; Powys LHB will remain. Originally commissioning bodies (except Powys, which also provided services), the LHBs' new remit will be wider. Seven trusts (already reduced from 14 to nine during 2008) will be abolished and their staff, property and functions brought under LHB control; the Welsh Ambulance Services Trust and Velindre Trust, which manages specialist oncology services, will remain. The main features of the new structure are:
- **National Advisory Board** – from April 2009 this will be chaired by the minister and comprise the deputy minister, NHS chief executive, chief medical officer, director of social services, three representatives of local government, third sector and trade unions, and two independent members. The board will be responsible for offering the minister independent advice; it will meet in public and publish its papers.
- **National Delivery Group** – from April 2009 this will be chaired by NHS Wales' chief executive and comprise the DHSS senior directors and up to three independent members; it will be responsible for LHBs' day-to-day operational performance.

- **Local health boards** – from October 2009 the seven LHBs will be responsible for planning, designing, developing and securing delivery of primary, community, hospital and specialised services: NHS Wales has more than 130 hospitals and 15,000 beds; each LHB will have a decision-making corporate board, a stakeholder reference group and a professional forum; LHB non-executives will include representatives of universities, local government, third sector, trade unions and five independent members.
- **Public Health Wales NHS Trust** – from October 2009 this trust will bring together in a single organisation a range of public health services and functions from a number of different organisations.

Commissioning will be replaced by a new planning system to 'integrate different elements of planning – service, workforce, estate and finance' and benefit from 'strong clinical engagement throughout'. Further work will be undertaken on whether the LHBs will be allocated some of the responsibilities of Health Commission Wales, the specialist commissioning body; a review of HCW in 2008 found it fell short of its fitness for purpose.

The future of Wales' 19 community health councils will be subject to consultation during 2009. The CHCs are statutory lay organisations with rights to information about, access to, and consultation with all NHS organisations on behalf of the public. The Welsh Assembly Government strengthened their powers in 2004.

The DHSS has set up the Bevan Commission to advise on emerging health issues. It aims to ensure NHS Wales 'can draw on the best practice from across the world while remaining true to the principles of the NHS as established by Aneurin Bevan', and will exist for up to two years.

**Further information**
*NHS Wales – present and future*, Welsh NHS Confederation, February 2008.
*A summary of comments on the proposed structural changes to NHS Wales*, Welsh NHS Confederation, June 2008.
*Health Commission Wales: a review*, Wales Centre for Health, June 2008.
*Delivering the new NHS for Wales: consultation paper II*, Welsh Assembly Government, December 2008.
*Unification of public health services in Wales: consultation paper*, January 2009.
Welsh NHS Confederation **www.welshconfed.org**

## NHS Wales structure

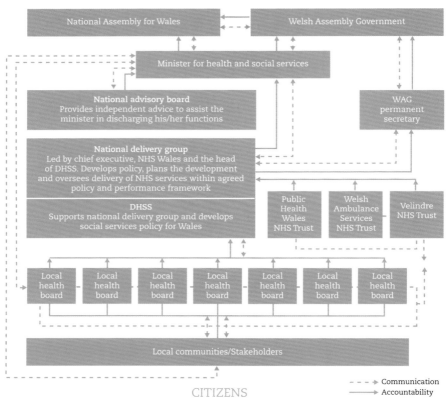

CITIZENS

National Assembly for Wales

Welsh Assembly Government

Minister for health and social services

**National advisory board**
Provides independent advice to assist the minister in discharging his/her functions

WAG permanent secretary

**National delivery group**
Led by chief executive, NHS Wales and the head of DHSS. Develops policy, plans the development and oversees delivery of NHS services within agreed policy and performance framework

**DHSS**
Supports national delivery group and develops social services policy for Wales

Public Health Wales NHS Trust

Welsh Ambulance Services NHS Trust

Velindre NHS Trust

Local health board

Local health board

Local health board

Local health board

Local health board

Local health board

Local health board

Local communities/Stakeholders

- - - → Communication
——→ Accountability

CITIZENS

Source: Welsh Assembly Government

## Vital statistics: **NHS Wales activity**

Every year NHS Wales:

- undertakes 700,000 first outpatient appointments
- treats 600,000 inpatients and day cases
- sees 1,059,000 people in A&E
- prescribes 53.9 million items
- carries out 655,000 eye tests.

Source: Welsh Assembly Government

**Organisations spanning England and Wales**

Organisations whose remit covers both England and Wales include:
- National Institute for Health and Clinical Excellence (see page 158)
- National Patient Safety Agency (see page 136)
- Health Protection Agency (see page 63)
- NHS Direct (see page 96)
- Medicines and Healthcare Products Regulatory Agency (see page 23).

## Strategy and policy

Although the NHS in Wales has had slightly different policy and structural arrangements from England for most of its existence, these have diverged more markedly since devolution in an attempt to find distinctively Welsh solutions for specifically Welsh problems. Wales has some of the UK's highest rates of cancer, heart disease and deprivation, while part of its population suffers the worst health status in Europe.

Following the 2007 Welsh Assembly election, Labour and Plaid Cymru as the ruling coalition drew up a policy document, *One Wales*. Its chapter on the NHS stated: 'We firmly reject the privatisation of NHS services or the organisation of such services on market models. We will guarantee public ownership, public funding and public control of this vital public service.'

It pledged that the Welsh Assembly Government's four-year programme would include:
- a review of reconfiguration
- elimination of the use of private hospitals by NHS Wales
- ruling out use of the private finance initiative in NHS Wales
- an end to competitive tendering for NHS cleaning contracts
- investment in 'multi-purpose well-being centres'
- a charter on patients' rights
- separate mental health legislation for Wales
- development of a rural health plan.

A moratorium on proposals for changing community hospitals was agreed, and a pledge made that changes to district general hospitals would only take place once new community services were in place. Some plans approved before the election were subsequently given the go-ahead while others remained under review.

## Recent milestones in Welsh health policy

### Putting patients first
Published in 1998, this abolished GP fundholding in Wales and set up local health groups as part of the existing five health authorities.

### Better health: better Wales
Also published in 1998, this explicitly linked poverty and ill health.

### Improving health in Wales – a plan for the NHS with its partners
The Welsh NHS plan published in January 2001, this proposed new structures: establishing the Health and Social Care Department, three regional offices and several other all-Wales bodies, as well as replacing the five health authorities and local health groups with 22 local health boards.

### Review of health and social care in Wales: the Wanless Report
The Welsh Assembly Government appointed Derek Wanless to examine how resources could be translated into reform and improved performance in health and social care. In July 2003 he recommended:
- a radical redesign for health and social care services
- an evidence-based approach to best practice and improving system performance
- developing capacity outside acute hospitals
- more public and patient involvement
- stronger performance-management systems.

### Designed for life: creating world-class health and social care for Wales in the 21st century
Updating Improving health in Wales, this is the Welsh Assembly Government's vision for the NHS up to 2015, influenced by the Wanless Report and published in May 2005.

### Delivering the new NHS for Wales: consultation paper II
Published in December 2008, this set out a new structure for an NHS Wales without the internal market (see page 254).

### Further information
*One Wales – a progressive agenda for the government of Wales: an agreement between the Labour and Plaid Cymru groups in the National Assembly*, Welsh Assembly Government, June 2007.

## Key targets and priorities

The annual operating framework, first issued in 2007/08, aims to help organisations improve services by setting out what the Welsh Assembly Government expects of them. It contains policy requirements, national targets and efficiency and productivity measures that must be achieved and maintained during the year ahead.

In 2009/10 the DHSS intends 'to balance the need to seek further service improvement with the challenges and demands of the NHS reform programme'. Areas for focus set out in the operating framework are:

- achieving national targets – on access and improving cancer, stroke, renal, cardiac, mental health, CAMHS and other services
- achieving efficiency – across nine measures, including length of stay
- achieving financial health – including 3 per cent efficiency savings
- achieving compliance with the Healthcare Standards for Wales.

Access 2009, NHS Wales' maximum waiting-time target of 26 weeks from referral to treatment, is due to be met by December 2009. Progress has been good, although doubts remain about the affordability of meeting the deadline.

### Further information

*NHS Wales: annual operating framework 2009/2010*, Welsh Assembly Government, December 2008.

**Spotlight on policy: Free prescriptions**

The Welsh Assembly Government was the first in the UK to abolish all prescription charges – from April 2007, having reduced them progressively since 2001. Scotland and Northern Ireland are following suit; in England charges are currently £7.20. Only those with a GP and a pharmacist in Wales can take advantage of the scheme. It is estimated the policy will benefit 1.5 million people who are not exempt from charges, and cost about £30 million a year.

# Financing NHS Wales

## Sources of funding

General taxation and national insurance contributions form the main source of funding for NHS Wales, as they do for the NHS in the rest of the UK. Charges and receipts from land sales or other assets add comparatively small sums to the total. The Welsh Assembly, unlike the Scottish Parliament, is unable to raise additional taxes.

## Resource allocation

UK Government spending reviews, which take place every two years and cover a three-year cycle, determine the amount of public expenditure available for Wales. Increases to the Welsh block grant are made according to the population-based Barnett formula, introduced in 1978 and modified slightly since devolution.

The Welsh Assembly Government then decides how this sum should be allocated among its departments, subject to the Assembly's approval. The health budget comprises seven expenditure groups:
- LHBs
- education and training – mainly for doctors and nurses
- family health services – GP pay and prescribing costs, plus dental and ophthalmic costs
- health improvement – public health initiatives, including immunisation
- health promotion – in schools, workplaces, local communities and the NHS
- food standards – funding the Welsh Executive of the Food Standards Agency
- welfare foods – free milk to children and expectant mothers on income support.

Allocations to LHBs are made using the Townsend formula devised in 2001. Its principal aim is to curb growth in health inequalities by better targeting NHS resources into areas of greatest need.

In 2009/10, health and social services account for £6 billion of the Welsh Assembly Government's £15 billion budget, representing a 3.3 per cent increase in NHS Wales' revenue budget.

The Wales Audit Office found in 2008 that NHS Wales had improved its financial management. All 22 LHBs were on budget at the end of 2007/08, although only after a cash injection of £24 million. Trusts had a £3 million deficit, much reduced from £14 million and £26 million in the previous two years.

**Further information**
*Are the devolved financial management arrangements in NHS Wales effective?* Wales Audit Office, September 2008.

## Staffing and human resources

### Staff numbers
About 90,000 people work in NHS Wales on a whole-time equivalent basis. Of these, 71,500 people are directly employed, while there are also 1,900 GPs, 1,100 general dental practitioners, 4,000 practice support staff and 600 opticians.

Staff include:
- 5,500 hospital doctors and dentists
- 28,000 nurses, midwives and health visitors
- 10,800 scientific, therapeutic and technical staff
- 9,500 healthcare assistants and other support staff
- 16,000 administration and estates staff
- 1,400 ambulance staff.

### Workforce planning
*Designed for life* noted that NHS Wales needed a new process for workforce planning and commissioning education – a strengthened, integrated and more streamlined model of whole-system workforce redesign. *Designed to work* aims to help bring about the staffing changes needed to achieve the goals of *Designed for life*, particularly cultural change and engaging clinical leaders.

**Further information**
*Making the connections: connecting the workforce: the workforce challenge for health*, Welsh Assembly Government, July 2005.
*Designed to work: a workforce strategy to deliver Designed for life*, Welsh Assembly Government, July 2006.

**National Leadership and Innovation Agency for Healthcare**

NLIAH was set up in 2005 to help build leadership capacity and capability underpinned by technology, innovation, leading-edge thinking and best practice. Its programme includes work on:

- innovative models of clinical leadership
- modernisation assessments across health communities
- collecting and disseminating best practice and ensuring its uptake.

All NLIAH's programmes are arranged under a series of brands which focus on a particular aspect of management and leadership development, service improvement or workforce development. These are:

- Care to Lead
- Design 4 Improvement
- Design 4 Learning
- Design 4 Partnership
- Good Governance in Health
- Modernisation assessment
- Quality improvement plan
- Skills 4 Change
- Workforce development.

**www.nliah.wales.nhs.uk**

**Welsh Partnership Forum**

The Welsh Partnership Forum consists of representatives of the 14 recognised healthcare trade unions for NHS Wales, senior managers from NHS Wales and representatives from the Welsh Assembly Government.

Its main purpose is developing, supporting and implementing workforce policies on national, regional and local levels. The Forum provides strategic leadership on partnership working between employers and employee representatives. It is involved in planning, education, recruitment, retention, development and support of NHS Wales staff.

# Information technology in NHS Wales

NHS Wales' IT strategy, Informing Healthcare, was launched in 2003. It will achieve its aims through a series of planned and agreed service improvement projects.

Informing Healthcare focuses on:

- **Single patient record**
  Every patient will have a single electronic health record, with the eventual aim of fully integrated health and social care records.
- **Workforce empowerment**
  All NHS Wales staff will be given access to new skills allowing them to use the new systems. Training will range from basic IT and information management to more specialist health informatics skills. This will enable them to take advantage of new productivity tools and computerised business support services. Employees will have access through the new HR system to their own staff record.
- **Patient empowerment**
  By providing better information about treatments, risks and benefits, patients will be able to play a more active role in decision-making about their treatments, and their satisfaction with services should increase.
- **Service improvement**
  Modernisation and IT in healthcare have not been well integrated. The Informing Healthcare strategy argues that they must be closely aligned both strategically and in practice.
- **Knowledge management**
  Knowledge management is concerned with collecting, making best use of and providing access to necessary information while minimising the collection of information that brings little benefit.

Informing Healthcare has a national programme board and an implementation board. Recent developments include:

- individual health record – implementation in out-of-hours care in two health communities
- clinical portal – a web gateway to give doctors and nurses access to clinical and administrative information systems
- My Health Online – to enable patients to access their own health information.

**Further information**

*Informing Healthcare achievements 2008: using information and technology for better patient care*, Informing Healthcare/NHS Wales, 2008.

*National infrastructure strategy for NHS Wales*, Informing Healthcare/NHS Wales, July 2008.

*Briefing: Investment in information technology – an investment in patient care*, Welsh NHS Confederation, November 2008.

Informing Healthcare **www.wales.nhs.uk/ihc**

## Health of Wales Information Service (HOWIS)

This website is the official gateway to online information about NHS Wales. **www.wales.nhs.uk**

# 13 The NHS in Northern Ireland

Direct rule from Westminster between 2002 and 2007 restricted the healthcare reform process in Northern Ireland, but a major restructure takes effect from April 2009. For more than 30 years, health and social services have been bound more closely together in Northern Ireland than in the rest of the UK, and together they are the Province's largest employer. Now that peace has been restored after more than three decades of the 'Troubles', Northern Ireland must begin to tackle in earnest its major health challenges. For example, it has some of the worst mental health problems in the UK and a particularly high suicide rate.

## The structure of the NHS in Northern Ireland

Since October 1973, the NHS in Northern Ireland has been integrated with social care and is known as the Health and Social Care services (HSC). Accountability is to the Northern Ireland Assembly at Stormont via the minister who heads the Department of Health, Social Services and Public Safety. Five health and social care trusts and an ambulance trust provide services commissioned by a single regional health and social care board. www.hscni.net

### Northern Ireland Assembly

The Northern Ireland Assembly was established as a result of the Belfast (or 'Good Friday') Agreement of 1998. It was elected later that year, operated in shadow form without government powers until full devolution in December 1999, but was then suspended in October 2002. Recalled in May 2006, under the St Andrews agreement it sat as a 'transitional assembly' to prepare for elections in March 2007 and restoration of full devolution in May 2007.

The Assembly has full legislative and executive authority for 'transferred matters', which include areas such as health, social care, education and agriculture. In addition, it may at a later date take responsibility for 'reserved matters', such as policing and criminal law. 'Excepted matters' remain the UK Parliament's responsibility, and include defence, foreign policy and taxation.

The Assembly has 108 members (MLAs), six from each of Northern Ireland's 18 Westminster constituencies. Currently they represent eight political parties. A First Minister and a Deputy First Minister are elected to lead the ten-strong Executive Committee of Ministers. They have to stand for election jointly, and to be elected must have cross-community support. The parties elected to the Assembly choose ministerial portfolios and select ministers in proportion to their party strength. The Executive Committee brings forward proposals for new legislation in the form of Executive Bills for the Assembly to consider. It also sets out a programme for government each year, with an agreed budget for approval by the Assembly.

Ten cross-party statutory committees have power to examine, debate and recommend changes to the Northern Ireland departments' policies and decisions. This includes, for example, how money is shared and spent. The health, social services and public safety committee advises and assists the minister of health, social services and public safety to formulate policy and undertakes scrutiny, policy development and consultation. It has 11 members.

Among the Assembly's six standing committees, the 11-strong public accounts committee's remit is to consider accounts covering the NHS in Northern Ireland. The committee has the power 'to send for persons, papers and records'.

The Northern Ireland Office, led by the Secretary of State for Northern Ireland, represents Northern Ireland's interests in the UK Government and Parliament. There are 18 MPs at Westminster representing Northern Ireland constituencies.
www.niassembly.gov.uk
www.nio.gov.uk

### Northern Ireland Executive
The Executive forms the government of Northern Ireland and comprises ten departments plus the Office of the First Minister and Deputy First Minister. Each department is headed by a minister who sits on the Assembly's Executive Committee. While devolution was suspended, the departments were run by the Northern Ireland Office.
www.northernireland.gov.uk

## Department of Health, Social Services and Public Safety (DHSSPS)

The DHSSPS's mission is to improve the health and social well-being of people in Northern Ireland – by ensuring the provision of appropriate health and social care services in hospitals, GPs' surgeries and the community, through nursing, social work and other professional services. It also leads a major programme of cross-government action to improve health and well-being and reduce health inequalities.

The DHSSPS is responsible for:
- health and social care – including policy and legislation for hospitals, family practitioner services, community health and personal social services
- public health – policy and legislation to promote and protect the health and well-being of Northern Ireland's population
- public safety – policy and legislation for food safety, emergency planning, fire and rescue services.

The permanent secretary is also chief executive of the health and social care system, as well as principal accounting officer for all the DHSSPS's responsibilities. Key business groups within the department are:
- resources and performance management group
- healthcare policy group
- social policy group
- office of the chief medical officer.

The DHSSPS also has a modernisation directorate and a human resources directorate. It has one executive agency, Health Estates.

In addition, five professional groups are each led by a chief professional officer:
- medical and allied services
- social services inspectorate
- nursing and midwifery advisory group
- dental services
- pharmaceutical advice and services.

The DHSSPS employs 1,000 people and is the largest of Northern Ireland's 10 departments, accounting for two-fifths of the Northern Ireland budget.

### Further information
*Business plan 2007/08*, DHSSPS, March 2007.
www.dhsspsni.gov.uk

## Restructuring health and social care in Northern Ireland

The Northern Ireland Assembly approved changes to the structure of health and social care in January 2009, for implementation in April 2009. The process began in 2005 while Northern Ireland was under direct rule from Westminster, when a new structure was proposed that would have reduced the Province's 47 health and social care organisations to 18. After devolution was restored, implementation was suspended while the proposals were reviewed and revised. Other reform models elsewhere in the UK and in the Republic of Ireland were taken into account in drawing up the new streamlined structure.

Five health and social care trusts (reduced in 2007 from 18) will continue. Changes comprise:

- the new Health and Social Care Board, replacing four health and social services boards, to focus on commissioning, resource management and performance management
- five local commissioning groups as statutory committees of the regional board, to involve primary care professionals in planning and resourcing services, covering the same geographical area as the five trusts. Membership includes four GPs, a pharmacist, dentist, four elected representatives, two social care professionals, a nurse, a public health professional, an allied health professional and two voluntary sector representatives
- the new Public Health Agency, incorporating the work of the Health Promotion Agency but with wider responsibility for health protection, health improvement to address health inequalities and public health issues
- the new Business Services Organisation, providing support functions for the entire system
- the new Patient and Client Council, replacing the health and social services councils, with five local offices operating in the same geographical areas as the trusts
- a smaller and more focused DHSSPS
- the Northern Ireland Regional Medical Physics Agency will be merged with the Belfast Health and Social Care Trust
- the Mental Health Commission's functions will transfer to the Regulation and Quality Improvement Authority.

### Further information

*Proposals for health and social care reform: consultation report,* DHSSPS, September 2008.

## New structure of HSC in Northern Ireland

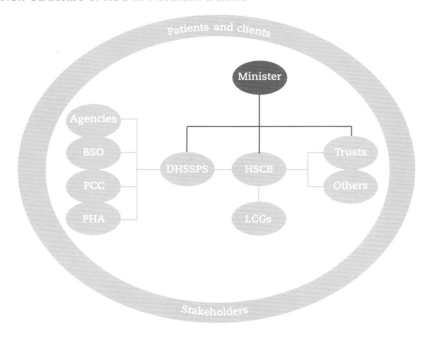

BSO: Business services organisation

PCC: Patient client council

PHA: Public Health Agency

HSCB: Health and social care board

LCGs: Local commissioning groups

Others: GPs, independent and private sector, voluntary and community

Source: DHSSPS

## Strategy and policy

Given Northern Ireland's unique geographical and political circumstances within the UK, it is to be expected that the NHS here has distinct characteristics – most notably that health and social care are integrated. While spending per head on health and social care is higher in Northern Ireland than in England, outputs and outcomes have lagged behind. Although this may be partly due to inefficiency, and therefore perhaps susceptible to reform, other reasons may include acknowledged greater needs, better quality of provision, the need to maintain hospitals in rural locations and the higher costs of delivering services in deprived areas.

### Recent milestones in Northern Ireland health policy

#### *Investing for health*
Published in 2002, this noted that health and well-being are largely determined by the social, economic, physical and cultural environment. This DHSSPS strategy document sought to shift emphasis from treating ill health to preventing it. It contained a framework for action to improve health and well-being and reduce health inequalities based on partnership.

#### *Developing better services: modernising hospitals and reforming structures*
Under the programme that resulted from this consultation document published in June 2002, Northern Ireland's 15 acute hospitals were to be replaced by a network of nine acute hospitals supported by seven local hospitals, with additional local hospitals in other locations as appropriate. The role of hospitals would be to support community-based care services in promoting health and well-being.

#### *A healthier future: a twenty-year vision for health and wellbeing in Northern Ireland 2005–2025*
Published in December 2004, this identified key policy directions, actions and outcomes that would contribute to achieving the vision. It built around five cross-cutting themes: investing for health and well-being; involving people; teams which deliver; responsive and integrated services and improving quality. A key element was reforming HPSS planning to become more integrated. Actions identified were intended to support implementation of *Investing for health*. Tackling chronic diseases and socio-economic disadvantage was the strategy's main focus.

#### *Independent review of health and social care services in Northern Ireland: the Appleby Report*
In the manner of the Wanless reports in England and Wales this report, published in August 2005, set out to examine the likely future resource needs of Northern Ireland's health and social services. It concluded that 'a significant increase in resources is required in the coming years, but with slower growth thereafter', but also that 'a significant underlying reason for current problems with the Northern Ireland health and social care sector relate to the use of resources rather than the amount of resources available'.

#### *Proposals for health and social care reform: consultation report*
Finalised blueprint for structural reform, published in September 2008 (see page 269).

## Key targets and priorities

The Northern Ireland Executive published at the beginning of 2008 its programme for government, in which promoting tolerance, inclusion, health and well-being is a priority. It acknowledged: 'The overall health status of our population needs urgent attention. We continue to have higher than average mortality from coronary heart disease, cancer and stroke, while obesity levels, particularly among our children, are rising at an alarming rate. Waiting times for treatment are still too long and the outcomes from treatment should be better. In mental health and learning disability, we are over-reliant on long-stay hospitals and the range of primary and community services is limited.'

Key goals include:
- by 2009 ensuring no one waits longer than nine weeks for a first outpatient appointment or diagnostic test, and 17 weeks for treatment – a cumulative reduction of 12 weeks from the present standard
- ensuring by 2013 that anyone with a mental health problem or learning disability is promptly and suitably treated in the community
- reducing mortality from bowel cancer by 15 per cent and acting to reduce cervical cancer by 70 per cent by 2013
- ensuring by 2013 that everyone who suffers a stroke is assessed for thrombolysis within 90 minutes, and reducing stroke mortality rates by 15 per cent
- by 2013 helping people with chronic illnesses to live more active lives and reducing unplanned hospital admissions for such patients by 50 per cent
- by 2011 reducing suicides by 15 per cent
- increasing to 125,000 the number of children and young people participating in sport and physical recreation by 2011
- at least a third of people with disabilities participating in sport and physical recreation by 2013
- reducing child poverty by 50 per cent by 2010.

In 2008 the Northern Ireland Audit Office reported that the DHSSPS was making 'good progress' on meeting key targets, with improved waiting times and survival rates for cancer and heart disease. However, health inequalities, suicide and obesity rates continued to need attention.

### Further information
*Programme for government*, Northern Ireland Executive, January 2008.
*The performance of the health service in Northern Ireland: report by the comptroller and auditor general*, NIAO, October 2008.

## Vital statistics: Inpatient admissions 2005/06 (per 1,000 population)

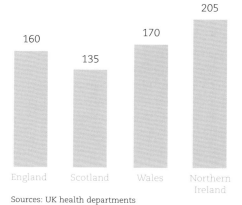

Sources: UK health departments

# Financing HSC in Northern Ireland

### Sources of funding

General taxation and national insurance contributions form the main source of funding for HSC in Northern Ireland, as they do for the NHS in the rest of the UK. Charges and receipts from land sales or other assets add comparatively small sums to the total. Like Wales and Scotland, Northern Ireland is phasing out prescription charges; currently £3, they will be abolished in 2010 at a cost of £13 million a year. The Northern Ireland Assembly, unlike the Scottish Parliament, is unable to raise additional taxes.

### Resource allocation

The Northern Ireland Executive sets targets for each of its departments in its programme for government.

Once the chancellor has announced the Northern Ireland settlement, each department submits a position report with its financial requirements to the Department of Finance and Personnel (DFP) and Office of the First Minister and Deputy First Minister. The DFP drafts a budget, which the Assembly considers alongside the draft programme for government. The Executive then revises the budget before deciding final allocations, which the Assembly debates and votes on.

The minister for health, social services and public safety then decides in detail how to allocate the department's resources for the coming year. The bulk is allocated to the boards to commission services from the trusts.

Allocations are made according to a weighted capitation formula which includes factors for demography, social deprivation and rurality. The allocation covers social services as well as health. The formula has been developed incrementally since the mid-1990s by the capitation formula review group. Some distinctive additional needs indicators are used in Northern Ireland, notably receipt of family credit and for maternity services, no previous births and multiple births.

The DHSSPS budget is divided among:
• hospital and community health services
• personal social services
• family health services.

The DHSSPS has the largest budget of any Northern Ireland department. DHSSPS revenue spending on health and personal social services in 2008/09 was £3.87 billion, rising to £4.19 billion in 2010/11. Capital spending is budgeted to rise from £174.7 million in 2007/08 to £189.2 million in 2010/11.

Every department has to achieve 3 per cent annual efficiency savings by 2010/11, amounting to £344 million for health and social care.

**Further information**
*Budget 2008–11*, Northern Ireland Executive, January 2008.
*Strategic resources framework 2008/09*, DHSSPS, February 2009.
www.pfgbudgetni.gov.uk

# Staffing and human resources

## Staff numbers

HSC is Northern Ireland's largest employer, accounting for just over 10 per cent of the Province's workforce. In 2008 it employed almost 77,000 people either full-time or part-time. These included:

- 3,885 medical and dental staff
- 16,140 qualified nurses and midwives
- 6,997 professional and technical staff
- 7,284 social care staff
- 1,025 ambulance staff
- 12,593 administrative and clerical staff

In addition, about 1,000 GPs work in Northern Ireland. In terms of headcount, staff increased by 7.3 per cent between 2004 and 2008.

## Workforce planning and pay

The DHSSPS's human resource directorate provides advice and guidance to HSC employers on pay and terms and conditions of employment for health and social care staff. The directorate comprises:

- education and training unit
- HSC superannuation branch
- pay and employment unit
- workforce planning unit.

Legislation requires the DHSSPS to ensure that pay rates in the HSC correspond as closely as possible to rates in the rest of the UK. This is known as the 'parity principle', and has existed in one form or another since 1949. Senior executives are the only staff group without a direct link to the comparable group in the rest of the UK, but this may change as a result of a current review by the Senior Salaries Review Body.

The workforce planning unit undertakes comprehensive workforce planning reviews regionally across the main professions and supporting groups so that the DHSSPS can judge the number of training places to commission. The workforce planning cycle comprises a major review of each group every three years, supported by annual update reviews.

## Information technology in HSC

The DHSSPS intends to invest £300 million over the next ten years for new and upgraded ICT systems across primary, secondary and community care. It will be aimed at improving record-keeping and sharing information between professional groups, while a medicines management system will be a foundation for electronic prescribing. A picture archiving and communications system will improve diagnostic imaging. Systems will be upgraded to ensure a better flow of information between primary and secondary care.

### HSC in Northern Ireland website

This website is the official gateway to the Health and Social Care services in Northern Ireland.
www.hscni.net

# 14 The NHS in Europe

The European Union now represents 27 countries and over 490 million people. It is governed by a series of treaties negotiated at intergovernmental conferences and ratified by each member state. Its work is carried out by different institutions – from the Council of Ministers to the European Commission, European Parliament and European Court of Justice.

The EU's work on health has developed substantially over the last 15 years. In the past, health policy was seen as very much the responsibility of member states, and little work took place at EU level, but since the beginning of the decade the EU has aimed for a more co-ordinated approach. Developments in the single European market and rulings in the European Court have also had an important impact on healthcare. The NHS needs to keep abreast of developments in Europe and seek to influence them when appropriate.

**Key organisation: NHS European Office**
The NHS European Office was opened in September 2007. Based in Brussels and London, and part of the NHS Confederation, it is funded by the strategic health authorities. Its aims are:
• monitoring policy and legislative developments important to the NHS
• keeping NHS organisations abreast of EU developments
• influencing EU proposals in the NHS's interest
• informing NHS organisations of funding opportunities
• promoting NHS priorities and interests to European institutions.

**Further information**
*NHS European Office: policy priorities 2009*, NHS European Office, January 2009.
**www.nhsconfed.org/europe**

## EU health policy
EU policy and legislative developments have a substantial impact on the NHS as a provider and commissioner of services, as a major employer in Europe and as a business. Developments in internal market rules, employment legislation, competition legislation and environment and energy policy and legislation must all be considered in parallel with EU health policy to determine potential implications for the NHS. Recent European Court rulings have clarified how EU internal market rules apply to health services, which will have a wide-reaching impact on the NHS.

# The European Union

## Member states

1 Austria
2 Belgium
3 Bulgaria
4 Cyprus
5 Czech Republic
6 Denmark
7 Estonia
8 Finland
9 France
10 Germany
11 Greece
12 Hungary
13 Ireland
14 Italy
15 Latvia
16 Lithuania
17 Luxembourg
18 Malta
19 Netherlands
20 Poland
21 Portugal
22 Romania
23 Slovakia
24 Slovenia
25 Spain
26 Sweden
27 United Kingdom

## Candidate countries

28 Croatia
29 Macedonia
30 Turkey

Source: Foreign Commonwealth Office

## European Parliament

This is the directly elected parliamentary body of the EU. With the Council of Ministers, it forms the legislative branch of the EU institutions. It has over 700 members, who are elected proportionally from the member states every five years. MEPs sit in political groups, and not as national delegations. Elections will take place in 2009, when the UK will choose 72 MEPs.
www.europarl.europa.eu

## Council of Ministers

Officially titled the Council of the European Union, this is composed of government representatives from each member state, and is presided over by whichever country holds the EU presidency at the time; the presidency changes on a six-month rotational basis. National ministers responsible for specific policy areas meet within the Council to discuss proposals from the European Commission. Health ministers from each of the 27 member states meet in the Health Council, which formally sits once during each presidency.
www.consilium.europa.eu

## European Commission

The Commission is the EU's executive body. It drafts policy proposals (regulations, directives, recommendations), presents them to the Council of Ministers and European Parliament for adoption and ensures that measures and actions are implemented. Since 2000 it has had a specific directorate for health and consumer protection. This is one of 24 directorates in total, each led by a European commissioner whose work is overseen by the president of the Commission.
http://ec.europa.eu

## European Court of Justice

Based in Luxembourg, the Court ensures that laws passed at a European level are applied and interpreted correctly. Some of its rulings have had an impact on member states' healthcare systems.
http://curia.europa.eu

### EU health strategy

The EU has had an official health strategy since 2000, which it revised in 2007. This sets the direction of EU activities in health by establishing some core principles: taking a value-driven approach, recognising the links between health and economic prosperity, integrating health in all policies and strengthening the EU's voice in global health. It also sets the main strategic objectives for action: fostering good health in an ageing Europe, protecting citizens from health threats and creating dynamic health systems and new technologies.

The strategy recognises that huge differences in health exist between and within member states. It affirms the importance of tackling health inequalities and working across different sectors. It also recognises the importance of patient empowerment and of focusing on health determinants.

### Further information

*Together for health: a strategic approach for the EU 2008–2013*, European Commission, October 2007.

## Cross-border healthcare

The European Commission published legal proposals in 2008 on the principles governing cross-border healthcare in the EU. They are still subject to negotiation, but could have a major impact on NHS organisations, especially in terms of administrative burdens and the ability to plan finances and capacity.

### The rise of cross-border healthcare

Cross-border care is a growing trend, particularly for countries in mainland Europe. Test cases in the European Court of Justice concerning patients seeking reimbursement for cross-border care have driven developments. One case concerned a UK patient who sought reimbursement from the NHS for £3,900 for a hip replacement carried out in France after being told she would have to wait a year for the operation in Britain.

Rulings have created an ambiguous situation, defending both citizens' right to seek healthcare abroad and the health systems' ability to defend financial stability. The court has stipulated that provisions in the EU's treaties on free movement of services apply to healthcare regardless of how it is organised or financed – and the court has confirmed this is so even for a tax-funded system like the NHS.

As a result, citizens have been unclear about their entitlement to healthcare abroad or how they might go about identifying, comparing and choosing providers. Member states are unclear about how they can regulate and plan their systems without creating unjustified obstacles to free movement.

## European Commission proposals

Underpinning the proposals is the rationale that it should be as easy as possible for patients who want to access healthcare abroad to do so, subject to the same conditions applying to treatment at home. The aim is to restate and elaborate existing rights established by the European Court, clarifying them for patients and those managing healthcare systems.

The draft directive outlines common principles for delivering healthcare in the EU, sets a framework of patients' rights to healthcare in another country and provides a framework for co-operation in areas such as e-health and health technology assessment. Key proposals include:

- NHS patients would have the right to seek healthcare in another EU country that they would have received under the NHS, and to be reimbursed up to the amount their treatment would have cost the NHS; patients would have to cover travel and other costs
- patients seeking treatment abroad would be subject to the same conditions applying to treatment at home: for example, NHS patients would need a GP referral to see a specialist
- prior authorisation could only be compulsory in certain circumstances: treatment must require an overnight stay in hospital and the outflow of patients must pose a serious risk to health service planning or finances
- clear criteria for refusing prior authorisation must be set in advance, and it could not be refused if a patient experienced 'undue delay'
- a national contact point for information on cross-border healthcare for both home and incoming patients would have to be set up
- new data collection requirements relating to cross-border healthcare would be enforced.

The NHS European Office is working with EU decision-makers to ensure NHS concerns about the proposals are considered before the directive is finalised.

### Further information

*Proposal for a directive of the European Parliament and of the Council on the application of patients' rights in cross-border healthcare*, European Commission, July 2008.
*Communication from the Commission: a Community framework on the application of patients' rights in cross-border healthcare*, European Commission, July 2008.
*Consultation 1: A European health service? The European Commission's proposals on cross-border healthcare*, NHS European Office, August 2008.
*Consultation on the European Commission's proposals for a directive on the application of patients' rights in cross-border healthcare*, DH, October 2008.

## Key issues for 2009

### Patient safety and HCAI

The European Commission has launched a 'patient safety package' that includes a recommendation and a communication on patient safety and prevention of healthcare-associated infections. The NHS European Office will seek to ensure proposals are in line with ongoing NHS initiatives.

### Information on pharmaceutical drugs

The European Commission is reviewing legislation governing what information pharmaceutical companies can provide to the public about prescription-only medicines. Proposed changes aim to address patients' increasing demand for such information, to reduce risk of them accessing misleading or poor-quality information and to mitigate unequal access to information throughout the EU. Concerns have been raised about potential pressures on prescribers and prescribing budgets. The NHS European Office will work with stakeholders throughout the legislative process to represent NHS interests.

### Organ donation and transplantation

The European Commission has published legal proposals on the quality and safety of transplant processes. These aim to ensure consistently high standards throughout the EU, with scope for each country to implement them as appropriate to its own system. Alongside a draft directive, the Commission has produced an action plan to increase organ availability by sharing best practice and enhancing the efficiency of transplantation systems. The NHS European Office will continue to work with key stakeholders, including NHS Blood and Transplant, to ensure as far as possible that developments complement existing arrangements in the UK.

## Employment

The NHS European Office and NHS Employers European team will continue to monitor developments in EU employment policy and law. These include an EU consultation on the health workforce, legal proposals to revise the directive on maternity leave and potential proposals for health and safety at work legislation to protect healthcare workers from blood-borne infections due to needlestick injuries. The NHS European Office will consider the implications for the NHS and engage with them as required.

## Public procurement and competition

The NHS European Office will brief NHS trusts on EU initiatives concerning public procurement and competition policy. It will promote EU guidance to boost green public procurement to trusts and advise them on new law affecting public procurement of clean vehicles. It will also assess the impact of EU competition rules on NHS activity and provide guidance on where NHS bodies may be considered to be engaged in 'economic activity' that renders them subject to EU competition law.

## Energy and environment

Recently proposed revisions to the directive on energy performance in buildings seek to improve minimum energy efficiency requirements for new and existing buildings. They also require the public sector to play a leading role in promoting energy efficiency. The proposals may have a considerable impact on the NHS as a major energy consumer with a large infrastructure. The European Commission has also proposed revisions to existing EU legislation on industrial pollution. These aim to strengthen and extend the scope of existing law to cover smaller combustion installations. This could have implications for about 70 NHS hospitals. In liaison with NHS organisations, the NHS European Office is shaping a response and will push for changes as required.

## Research and innovation

The European Year of Creativity and Innovation takes place in 2009. In the light of this and the NHS's new priorities in research and innovation, the NHS European Office will monitor developments and advise on opportunities to access EU funding that NHS organisations with an R&D interest can apply for.

# 15   The NHS: a brief history

## Before the NHS

At the beginning of the 20th century, a network of charitable, voluntary and local authority hospitals had developed, but it was inadequate for a rapidly growing population. Charitable and voluntary hospitals dealt mainly with serious illnesses, while municipal health services comprised maternity hospitals, hospitals for infectious diseases like smallpox and tuberculosis and hospitals for elderly, mentally ill and mentally handicapped people.

The social reformer, Beatrice Webb, is often credited with being the first to call for a national health service, in 1909. A compromise was achieved in the 1911 National Insurance Act, under which wage-earners below a certain income received sickness benefit and treatment from doctors who contracted their services to local 'panels'. Workers' families were not covered. Outside the scheme, medical treatment had to be paid for – often according to what the patient could afford. As a result, many hospitals were brought to the brink of financial ruin.

Over the next 30 years, several developments paved the way for the NHS. In 1919 the Ministry of Health was established, and a Scottish Board of Health created to improve public health and encourage research, treatment and medical training. In the following year, the Dawson Report called for a single authority to oversee a comprehensive medical treatment system. Gradually throughout the 1920s and 1930s, the idea of a national system of publicly funded healthcare began to gain momentum.

With the outbreak of war it became a national priority, and the Emergency Medical Service was set up, giving the Government control over voluntary and municipal hospitals as well as responsibility for their funding. In 1942 the Beveridge Report described a vision for welfare reform based on eradication of the five giants of idleness, squalor, hunger, disease and ignorance. The coalition Government's 1944 white paper stated that the aims of a new health service would be:

> to ensure that in future every man and woman and child can rely on getting all the advice and treatment and care which they may need in matters of personal health; that what they get shall be the best medical and other facilities available; that their getting these shall not depend on whether they can pay for them, or any other factor irrelevant to the real need.

## Early days

After the war, the Attlee Government's blueprint for the NHS described a public service more ambitious than any other western democracy's. It was to be universal – covering everyone; comprehensive – offering 'all necessary forms of healthcare'; and free at the point of use – funded from taxes. The proposal aroused widespread public enthusiasm, and for many enabled access to specialist services from which they had been excluded. The then Health Minister, Aneurin Bevan, called it 'the most civilised achievement of modern government'. The country was convinced it was creating 'the finest health service in the world'.

The NHS began throughout the UK on 5 July 1948. All voluntary and municipal hospitals were nationalised and overseen in England by 14 regional hospital boards, supported by 35 teaching hospital boards, which reported directly to the Ministry of Health. These boards supervised 400 hospital management committees, while 117 executive councils ran primary care services; local authorities were responsible for community care. Hospital doctors, nurses and other staff became state employees, although GPs remained independent and contracted their services to the NHS.

In theory, Bevan's system was intended to allow provision to meet demand. But initial funding failed to take account of the problems the service inherited, the unfair distribution of resources or the need to raise standards. No one had anticipated how demand would explode once long unmet needs could be satisfied. Soon the Government introduced dental, optical and prescription charges.

With funding capped during its formative years, the NHS had to rely on efficiency gains and increases in charges to expand services. The Conservative Government commissioned an inquiry into NHS costs, but the 1956 Guillebaud Report found little justification for charges and called for more resources to modernise hospitals and community care – to no avail. The NHS's rate of growth fell behind other health services, yet by 1958 *The Times* could declare: 'The nation has good reason to be proud of the NHS.'

## Reorganisation and reform

In 1962, Health Minister Enoch Powell's Hospital Plan proposed developing district general hospitals in England to serve populations of 125,000 in recognition that the NHS's ageing and neglected infrastructure was inadequate for modern healthcare. In the same year, the Porritt Report suggested the NHS should break down the divisions between primary, secondary and community care, but the administrative structure was to remain intact until 1974.

The major reorganisation of that year – devised by a Conservative Government, but introduced by a Labour one – saw the formation in England of 14 regional health authorities and 90 area health authorities, which managed 206 district management teams. Teaching hospitals lost their separate status, while family practitioner committees were set up to oversee primary care. Community health councils were introduced to represent patients. Meanwhile, Scotland abolished its regional tier and set up central service organisations to carry out its functions. In the previous year, Northern Ireland had created the four health and social services boards that survived until 2009. The Welsh Hospital Board and 15 hospital management committees were replaced by eight health authorities coterminous with new local authorities. Everywhere, consensus management was the ruling philosophy.

England's area health authorities were short-lived, abolished in the next reorganisation of 1982 – devised and implemented by a Conservative Government – which created 192 district health authorities in their stead. Government dissatisfaction with consensus management – perceived to have given professional groups a veto over change – led to the beginning of a cultural upheaval with the Griffiths Report of 1983, which recommended general management replace consensus from top to bottom. In England and Wales, general managers at regional, district and unit level superseded consensus management teams, while an NHS Management Board within the Department of Health co-ordinated management nationally. Scotland and Northern Ireland followed suit a year later.

### Funding crises and further reform
Repeated funding crises in the late 1980s – compounding underfunding from the 1970s – led to Prime Minister Margaret Thatcher's year-long review of the service that culminated in *Working for patients*, the 1989 white paper which heralded the introduction of the NHS internal market in 1991 in England, a year later in Scotland and Wales and subsequently in Northern Ireland. The 'purchasers' of healthcare – health authorities and some GP practices that became known as 'fundholders' – were separated from the 'providers' such as hospitals, ambulance and community services, which were formed into NHS trusts with a measure of self-

government to compete with each other. The NHS Management Board became the NHS Executive, regional health authorities were reduced in number and family practitioner committees were replaced with family health services authorities.

In 1996, England's regional health authorities were swept away altogether in favour of regional offices of the NHS Executive, run by civil servants rather than NHS staff. Unified health authorities were created from the old districts and family health services authorities. In Wales, the nine existing health authorities and 18 family practitioner authorities were reconfigured into five new health authorities.

### Into the 21st century

Pledging to abolish the internal market and GP fundholding on its election in 1997, the Labour Government sought a 'third way' of running the NHS, based on partnership and performance management. It involved yet more reorganisation. In England 500 primary care groups (later to become 300 primary care trusts, with additional powers) subsumed fundholding, and new bodies such as the National Institute for Clinical Excellence and Commission for Health Improvement (succeeded by the Healthcare Commission and now the Care Quality Commission) took prominent roles. Health action zones were to encourage co-operation between health and social services, while community health services trusts were generally merged with PCGs. Wales established local health groups to replace fundholding, while Scotland introduced local healthcare co-operatives and its own version of primary care trusts. Devolution in 1999 meant the NHS in Scotland, Wales and Northern Ireland began to diverge – quite markedly in some policy areas – from the service in England.

The persistence of funding crises led to a large NHS spending increase in the 2000 Budget and further reform outlined in the NHS Plan later that year. The Wanless review's costing of future health needs led to another massive increase in the 2002 Budget and further waves of reform. Yet more restructuring came with the advent of 28 strategic health authorities in England, replacing the 100 unified health authorities; the SHAs were reduced to ten and the 300 PCTs halved in number in 2006. Other initiatives – such as patient choice, payment by results and foundation trusts – are still working their way through the system. Restructuring took place in Wales in 2004, in Scotland in 2005 and in Northern Ireland in 2009, when NHS Wales restructured once again.

Political change in 2007 brought a new prime minister, administrations of a slightly different political complexion in Scotland and Wales and restoration of devolution in Northern Ireland. On the NHS's 60th anniversary in 2008, the Government published the findings of its Next Stage Review of the NHS in England.

**Further information**
*Sixty years of the National Health Service: a proud past and a healthy future*, DH, July 2008.
*Extraordinary: a snapshot of the NHS at 60*, NHS Employers, October 2008.
History of NHSScotland **www.60yearsofnhsscotland.co.uk**

**Milestones**
**1946** NHS Act becomes law
**1948** NHS begins
         First successful internal heart surgery
         Introduction of streptomycin for TB
**1952** First prescription charge introduced
**1953** Heart-lung machine invented
**1954** First kidney transplant
**1958** Smoking identified as cause of lung cancer
**1959** Polio immunisation introduced
         Mental Health Act signals reform of long-stay institutions
**1961** Contraceptive pill available on the NHS
**1962** The Hospital Plan published
         Porritt recommends unification of hospitals, health authorities and general practices
**1967** Abortion Act becomes law
**1968** Britain's first successful heart transplant
**1973** First CAT scan
**1974** Regional and area health authorities, family practitioner committees and community health councils established
**1979** Royal Commission on the NHS publishes its report
**1980** Black reports on health inequalities
**1982** Area health authorities abolished and 192 district health authorities created
**1983** Griffiths recommends introduction of general management
         Private contractors tender for NHS cleaning, catering and laundering services
**1984** AIDS virus discovered
         'Limited list' of drugs introduced to encourage generic prescribing
**1985** Cervical screening programme begins

**1986**  National campaign to prevent the spread of AIDS

**1988**  Department of Health and Social Security split into two separate departments

**1989**  *Working for patients* white paper heralds the internal market
Ambulance staff begin pay dispute

**1991**  Patient's Charter introduced

**1993**  Trade union Unison created from merger of NUPE, NALGO and COHSE

**1994**  14 regional health authorities reduced to eight

**1997**  NHS Primary Care Act

**1999**  Scottish Parliament, Welsh Assembly and NI Assembly take responsibility for NHS

**2000**  NHS Plan published
*Our national health* published in Scotland
GP Harold Shipman convicted of murdering 15 patients

**2002**  Wanless Report on future healthcare spending needs

**2003**  Community health councils abolished in England
New GP and consultant contracts agreed
NHS Wales restructured

**2004**  First foundation trusts established
NHSScotland abolishes trusts

**2005**  *Creating a patient-led NHS* published
NHSScotland creates community health partnerships
*Delivering for health* white paper published in Scotland

**2006**  *Our health, our care, our say* white paper published in England
28 strategic health authorities reduced to ten and 303 PCTs reduced to 152
Scotland bans smoking in public places

**2007**  England, Wales and Northern Ireland ban smoking in public places

**2008**  The NHS celebrates its 60th anniversary
Health minister Lord Darzi publishes the findings of his Next Stage Review

**2009**  Care Quality Commission replaces three inspectorates
Health and social care in Northern Ireland are restructured
NHS Wales is restructured again.

To mark the NHS's 60th anniversary, Children's Laureate Michael Rosen published a poem celebrating the service:

## These Are The Hands

These are the hands
That touch us first
Feel your head
Find the pulse
And make your bed.

These are the hands
That tap your back
Test the skin
Hold your arm
Wheel the bin
Change the bulb
Fix the drip
Pour the jug
Replace your hip

These are the hands
That fill the bath
Mop the floor
Flick the switch
Soothe the sore
Burn the swabs
Give us a jab
Throw out sharps
Design the lab.

And these are the hands
That stop the leaks
Empty the pan
Wipe the pipes
Carry the can
Clamp the veins
Make the cast
Log the dose
And touch us last.

# Acronym buster

| | |
|---|---|
| **ABPI** | Association of the British Pharmaceutical Industry |
| **AC** | Audit Commission |
| **ACAD** | ambulatory care and diagnostic unit |
| **ACCEA** | Advisory Committee on Clinical Excellence Awards |
| **ACDP** | Advisory Committee on Dangerous Pathogens |
| **ACEVO** | Association of Chief Executives of Voluntary Organisations |
| **ACGT** | Advisory Committee on Generic Testing |
| **ACRA** | Advisory Committee on Resource Allocation |
| **A&E** | accident and emergency |
| **AHP** | allied health professional |
| **AHSC** | academic health science centre |
| **ALB** | arm's-length body |
| **AM** | Assembly Member (Wales) |
| **ASCT** | asylum-seeker co-ordination team (Department of Health) |
| **BAMM** | British Association of Medical Managers |
| **BMA** | British Medical Association |
| **BME** | black and minority ethnic |
| **CAA** | comprehensive area assessment |
| **CAMHS** | child and adolescent mental health services |
| **CAT** | computerised axial tomography (scan) |
| **CDO** | chief dental officer |
| **CDU** | clinical decision unit |
| **CEAC** | Clinical and Excellence Awards Committee (Northern Ireland) |
| **CEMACH** | Confidential Enquiry into Maternal and Child Health |
| **CFH** | (NHS) Connecting for Health |
| **CHC** | community health council |
| **CHCP** | community health and care partnership (Scotland) |
| **CHD** | coronary heart disease |
| **CHI** | community health index (Scotland) |
| **CHIQ** | Centre for Health Information Quality |
| **CHMS** | community health and miscellaneous services |
| **CHP** | community health partnership (Scotland) |
| **CHRE** | Council for Healthcare Regulatory Excellence |
| **CIC** | community interest company |
| **CIMP** | clinical information management programme |
| **CIO** | chief information officer |
| **CIP** | cost improvement programme |
| **CLG** | (Department of) Communities and Local Government |
| **CMB** | corporate management board (Department of Health) |

| | |
|---|---|
| **CME** | continuing medical education |
| **CMHT** | community mental health team |
| **CMIC** | corporate management and improvement committee (Department of Health) |
| **CMO** | chief medical officer |
| **CNO** | chief nursing officer |
| **CNST** | Clinical Negligence Scheme for Trusts |
| **CO** | Cabinet Office |
| **COMARE** | Committee on Medical Aspects of Radiation in the Environment |
| **COMEAP** | Committee on the Medical Effects of Air Pollutants |
| **COSLA** | Convention of Scottish Local Authorities |
| **CPA** | care programme approach |
| **CPD** | continuing professional development |
| **CPR** | Child Protection Register |
| **CQC** | Care Quality Commission |
| **CQUIN** | commissioning for quality and innovation |
| **CRD** | Centre for Research and Dissemination |
| **CRHP** | Council for the Regulation of Healthcare Professionals |
| **CRS** | (NHS) Care Records Service |
| **CSA** | Common Services Agency |
| **CSCI** | Commission for Social Care Inspection |
| **CSM** | Committee on the Safety of Medicines |
| **CSR** | comprehensive spending review |
| **CTO** | compulsory treatment order |
| **DAT** | drug action team |
| **DCSF** | Department for Children, Schools and Families |
| **DDRB** | doctors and dentists (pay) review body |
| **DEFRA** | Department for Environment, Food and Rural Affairs |
| **DFP** | Department of Finance and Personnel (Northern Ireland) |
| **DFT** | distance from target |
| **DGH** | district general hospital |
| **DH or DoH** | Department of Health |
| **DHSSPS** | Department of Health, Social Services and Public Safety (Northern Ireland) |
| **DIUS** | Department for Innovation, Universities and Skills |
| **DMB** | departmental management board (Department of Health) |
| **DMS** | Defence Medical Services |
| **DPH** | director of public health |
| **DPHHP** | Department for Public Health and Health Professions (Wales) |
| **DPR** | Data Protection Registrar |
| **DRE** | Delivering race equality |

| | |
|---|---|
| DSO | departmental strategic objective |
| DSU | day surgery unit |
| DTC | diagnosis and treatment centre |
| DWP | Department for Work and Pensions |
| E&D | equality and diversity |
| EBH | evidence-based healthcare |
| EBM | evidence-based medicine |
| EBS | emergency bed service |
| ECCT | extended community care team (NHSScotland) |
| ECHR | European Convention on Human Rights |
| ECJ | European Court of Justice |
| ECN | extended choice network |
| EFL | external financing limit |
| e-GIF | electronic Government Interoperability Framework |
| EHPF | European Health Policy Forum |
| EHR | electronic health record |
| EHRG | equality and human rights group (Department of Health) |
| ENT | ear, nose and throat |
| EO | employers' organisation |
| EPP | Expert Patient Programme |
| EPR | electronic patient record |
| EPS | electronic prescription service |
| ERDIP | Electronic Record Development and Implementation Programme |
| ESR | electronic staff record |
| ETP | electronic transmission of prescriptions |
| ETS | emissions trading scheme (EU) |
| EWTD | European working-time directive |
| FCE | finished consultant episode |
| FCN | free choice network |
| FESC | Framework for procuring External Support for Commissioners |
| FHS | family health services |
| FMP | financial management programme |
| FOI | freedom of information |
| FPNC | free personal and nursing care (NHSScotland) |
| FSA | Food Standards Agency |
| FT | foundation trust |
| GDC | General Dental Council |
| GMC | General Medical Council |
| GMS | general medical services |
| GO | Government Office (of the English Regions) |

| | |
|---|---|
| **GPC** | (BMA) General Practitioners Committee |
| **GPSI** or **GPwSI** | general practitioner with a special interest |
| **GSCC** | General Social Care Council |
| **GTAC** | Gene Therapy Advisory Committee |
| **GTN** | (UK) Genetic Testing Network |
| **GWC** | General Whitley Council |
| **HA** | health authority |
| **HAZ** | health action zone |
| **HB** | health board |
| **HCAI** | healthcare-associated infection |
| **HCHS** | hospital and community health services |
| **HCSU** | Health Care Standards Unit |
| **HCW** | Health Commission Wales |
| **HDA** | Health Development Agency |
| **HDL** | Health Department letter |
| **HEAT** | health efficiency access treatment (targets – Scotland) |
| **HEFCE** | Higher Education Funding Council for England |
| **HES** | hospital episode statistics |
| **HFEA** | Human Fertilisation and Embryology Authority |
| **HIA** | health impact assessment |
| **HIC** | Health Innovation Council |
| **HIMP** | health improvement and modernisation plan |
| **HIW** | Health Inspectorate Wales |
| **HLC** | healthy living centre |
| **HLE** | healthy life expectancy |
| **HMO** | health maintenance organisation (USA) |
| **HOWIS** | Health of Wales Information Service |
| **HPA** | Health Protection Agency |
| **HPC** | Health Professions Council |
| **HPMA** | Healthcare People Management Association |
| **HQIP** | Healthcare Quality Improvement Partnership |
| **HRG** | healthcare resource group |
| **HSC** | (House of Commons) health select committee |
| **HSCI** | health service cost index |
| **HSCT** | health and social care trust (Northern Ireland) |
| **HSCT** | High Secure Commissioning Team |
| **HSE** | Health Survey for England |
| **HSRN** | Health Services Research Network |
| **HTA** | health technology assessment |
| **IAPT** | improving access to psychological therapies |

| | |
|---|---|
| IC | information commissioner |
| ICAS | independent complaints advocacy service |
| ICD | international classification of diseases |
| ICO | integrated care organisation |
| ICP | integrated care pathway |
| ICR | (NHS) injury costs recovery (scheme) |
| ICT | information and communication technology |
| ICU | intensive care unit |
| IMCA | independent mental capacity advocate |
| IM&T | information management and technology |
| IP | inpatient |
| IPR | individual performance review |
| IRP | independent reconfiguration panel |
| ISB | (NHS) Information Standards Board |
| ISD | Information and Statistics Division (Scotland) |
| ISTC | independent sector treatment centre |
| IWL | Improving Working Lives |
| JIPs | joint investment plans |
| JSNA | joint strategic needs assessment |
| KSF | (NHS) Knowledge and Skills Framework |
| LAL | local authority letter |
| LDP | local delivery plan |
| LGA | Local Government Association |
| LHB | local health board (Wales) |
| LHP | local health plan |
| LINk | local involvement network |
| LIS | local implementation strategy |
| LPSA | local public service agreement |
| LSP | local strategic partnership |
| LTA | long-term agreement |
| MAU | medical assessment unit |
| MCO | managed care organisation |
| MCN | managed clinical network |
| MFF | market forces factor |
| MHAC | Mental Health Act Commission |
| MHRA | Medicines and Healthcare Products Regulatory Agency |
| MHRT | mental health review tribunal |
| MLA | Member of the Legislative Assembly (Northern Ireland) |
| MMC | Modernising Medical Careers |
| MMR | measles, mumps, rubella |
| MPIG | minimum practice income guarantee |

| | |
|---|---|
| MRC | Medical Research Council |
| MRI | magnetic resonance imaging |
| MRSA | methicillin-resistant *Staphylococcus aureus* |
| MSP | Member of the Scottish Parliament |
| MTS | (NHS) management training scheme |
| N3 | New National Network |
| NAO | National Audit Office |
| NAW | National Assembly for Wales |
| NBA | National Blood Authority |
| NBAP | National Booked Admissions Programme |
| NBI | national beds inquiry |
| NCAAG | National Clinical Audit Advisory Group |
| NCAF | National Clinical Audit Forum |
| NCAPOP | National Clinical Audit and Patients' Outcomes Programme |
| NCAS | National Clinical Assessment Service |
| NCASP | National Clinical Audit Support Programme |
| NCE | national confidential enquiry |
| NCEPOD | National Confidential Enquiry into Perioperative Deaths |
| NCG | National Commissioning Group |
| NCVO | National Council for Voluntary Organisations |
| NDPB | non-departmental public body |
| NEAT | new and emerging applications of technology |
| NED | non-executive director |
| NES | NHS Education for Scotland |
| NHSI | NHS Institute for Innovation and Improvement |
| NHSL | NHS Logistics |
| NHSLA | NHS Litigation Authority |
| NHS LIFT | NHS Local Improvement Finance Trust |
| NHS QIS | NHS Quality Improvement Scotland |
| NHST | NHS trust |
| NIA | Northern Ireland Assembly |
| NIC | national insurance contribution |
| NICE | National Institute for Health and Clinical Excellence |
| NIGB | National Information Governance Board |
| NIHR | National Institute for Health Research |
| NIMHE | National Institute for Mental Health in England |
| NIO | Northern Ireland Office |
| NLH | National Library for Health |
| NLIAH | National Leadership and Innovation Agency for Healthcare (Wales) |
| NLOP | National Programme for IT local ownership programme |
| NMC | Nursing and Midwifery Council |

| | |
|---|---|
| **NOF** | New Opportunities Fund |
| **NOG** | National Oversight Group (for high-security hospitals) |
| **NPfIT** | National Programme for IT (in the NHS) |
| **NPG** | national priorities guidance |
| **NPHS** | National Public Health Service (Wales) |
| **NPSA** | National Patient Safety Agency |
| **NQB** | National Quality Board |
| **NRAC** | NHSScotland Resource Allocation Committee |
| **NRCI** | national reference cost index |
| **NRPB** | National Radiological Protection Board |
| **NRT** | nicotine replacement therapy |
| **NSCG** | National Specialist Commissioning Group |
| **NSF** | national service framework |
| **NSRC** | national schedule of reference costs |
| **NSS** | National Services Scotland |
| **NTA** | National Treatment Agency (for Substance Misuse) |
| **NTO** | national training organisation |
| **NWP** | (NHS) National Workforce Projects |
| **OCPA** | Office of the Commissioner for Public Appointments |
| **ODP** | operating department practitioner |
| **OFMDFM** | Office of the First Minister & Deputy First Minister (N. Ireland) |
| **OGC** | Office of Government Commerce |
| **OHE** | Office of Health Economics |
| **ONS** | Office for National Statistics |
| **OP** | outpatient |
| **OSC** | (local authority) overview and scrutiny committee |
| **OSCHR** | Office for Strategic Co-ordination of Health Research |
| **OSHA** | Office of the Strategic Health Authorities |
| **OT** | occupational therapist/therapy |
| **OTC** | over-the-counter |
| **OTS** | Office of the Third Sector |
| **PAC** | (House of Commons) public accounts committee |
| **PACS** | picture archiving and communications systems |
| **PAF** | performance assessment framework |
| **PALS** | patient advice and liaison service |
| **PASA** | (NHS) Purchasing and Supply Agency |
| **PBC** | practice-based commissioning |
| **PbR** | payment by results |
| **PCIP** | primary care investment plan |
| **PCO** | primary care organisation |
| **PCT** | primary care trust |

| | |
|---|---|
| PDP | personal development plan |
| PEC | professional executive committee (of PCT) |
| PFI | private finance initiative |
| PHeL | Public Health electronic Library |
| PHO | public health observatory |
| PMETB | Postgraduate Medical Education and Training Board |
| PMS | personal medical services |
| PPA | Prescription Pricing Authority |
| PPC | (prescription) pre-payment certificate |
| PPF | priorities and planning framework |
| PPI | patient and public involvement |
| PPIF | patient and public involvement forum |
| PPO | preferred provider organisation |
| PPP | public–private partnership |
| PPRS | Pharmaceutical Price Regulation Scheme |
| PRB | pay review body |
| PROM | patient-reported outcome measure |
| PRP | policy research programme |
| PSA | public service agreement |
| QA | quality assurance |
| QALY | quality-adjusted life year |
| QMAS | quality management and analysis system |
| QOF | quality and outcomes framework |
| QQUIP | Quest for Quality and Improved Performance |
| RAB | resource accounting and budgeting |
| RCD | research capacity development |
| RCN | Royal College of Nursing |
| RCP | Royal College of Physicians |
| RCPE | Royal College of Physicians of Edinburgh |
| RCPSG | Royal College of Physicians and Surgeons of Glasgow |
| RCS | Royal College of Surgeons |
| RCSE | Royal College of Surgeons of Edinburgh |
| RCT | randomised controlled trial |
| RGH | rural general hospital (NHSScotland) |
| ROCR | Review of Central Returns |
| RTA | road traffic accident |
| SACDA | Scottish Advisory Committee on Distinction Awards |
| SARS | severe acute respiratory syndrome |
| SAS | Scottish Ambulance Service |
| SAS | staff and associated specialist (doctors) |
| SASM | Scottish Audit of Surgical Mortality |

| | |
|---|---|
| **SBS** | (NHS) Shared Business Services |
| **SCG** | specialised commissioning group |
| **SCI** | Scottish care information |
| **SCVO** | Scottish Council for Voluntary Organisations |
| **SDO** | service delivery and organisation |
| **SDU** | (NHS) Sustainable Development Unit |
| **SEIF** | Social Enterprise Investment Fund |
| **SES** | single equality scheme (Department of Health) |
| **SEU** | Social Exclusion Unit |
| **SFA** | statement of fees and allowances |
| **SHA** | strategic health authority (and special health authority) |
| **SHO** | senior house officer |
| **SHOW** | Scottish Health on the Web |
| **SHRINE** | Strategic Human Resources Information Network |
| **SIGN** | Scottish Intercollegiate Guidelines Network |
| **SLA** | service level agreement |
| **SMAC** | Standing Medical Advisory Committee |
| **SMC** | Scottish Medicines Consortium |
| **SMR** | standardised mortality ratio |
| **SNMAC** | Standing Nursing and Midwifery Advisory Committee |
| **SNOMED** | systematised nomenclature of medicine |
| **SRB** | single regeneration budget |
| **SSA** | standard spending assessment |
| **SSC** | shared service centre |
| **ST&T** | scientific, therapeutic and technical (staff) |
| **TUPE** | Transfer of Undertakings (Protection of Employment ) Regulations 1981 |
| **UKCC** | UK Cochrane Centre |
| **UKCRC** | UK Clinical Research Collaboration |
| **UKCRN** | UK Clinical Research Network |
| **VFM** | value for money |
| **WAG** | Welsh Assembly Government |
| **WCH** | Wales Centre for Health |
| **WHO** | World Health Organisation |
| **WIsH** | Welsh Innovations in Healthcare |
| **WORD** | Wales Office of Research and Development (for Health and Social Care) |
| **WPF** | Welsh Partnership Forum |
| **WRT** | Workforce Review Team |
| **WTD** | working-time directive |

# Index

# Acknowledgements

The NHS Confederation is grateful to all those involved in the production of this edition of the *NHS handbook* (formerly known as the *pocket guide*). Particular thanks are due to:

- our sponsor, the Appointments Commission
- those who have supported the guide through advertising (listed below)
- those organisations that have kindly allowed us to reproduce diagrams and other materials
- Caroline Ball and John Cox for their expert editing and proofreading
- Grade Design, for designing and typesetting this year's handbook and for also designing the front cover.

We are also grateful to our members and other customers who have provided valuable feedback on previous editions of the *pocket guide*, to enable us to make year-on-year improvements.

### List of advertisers
NHS Institute for Innovation and Improvement (inside front cover)
Appointments Commission (back cover)

### The author
Peter Davies is a freelance writer and editor. He has written extensively on health policy and management issues, for which he won a major award from the Medical Journalists Association. He was editor of *Health Service Journal* from 1993 to 2002, and has contributed a regular column to *Guardian Unlimited*. He is married with two children and lives in London.